NATURAL ENVIRONMENT RESEARCH COUNCIL

INSTITUTE OF GEOLOGICAL SCIENCES

Geological Survey and Museum

BRITISH REGIONAL GEOLOGY

The Hampshire Basin and Adjoining Areas

THIRD EDITION

by

C. P. CHATWIN, M.Sc.

LONDON
HER MAJESTY'S STATIONERY OFFICE
1960

CONTENTS

ILLUSTRATIONS

FIGURES IN TEXT

PLATES

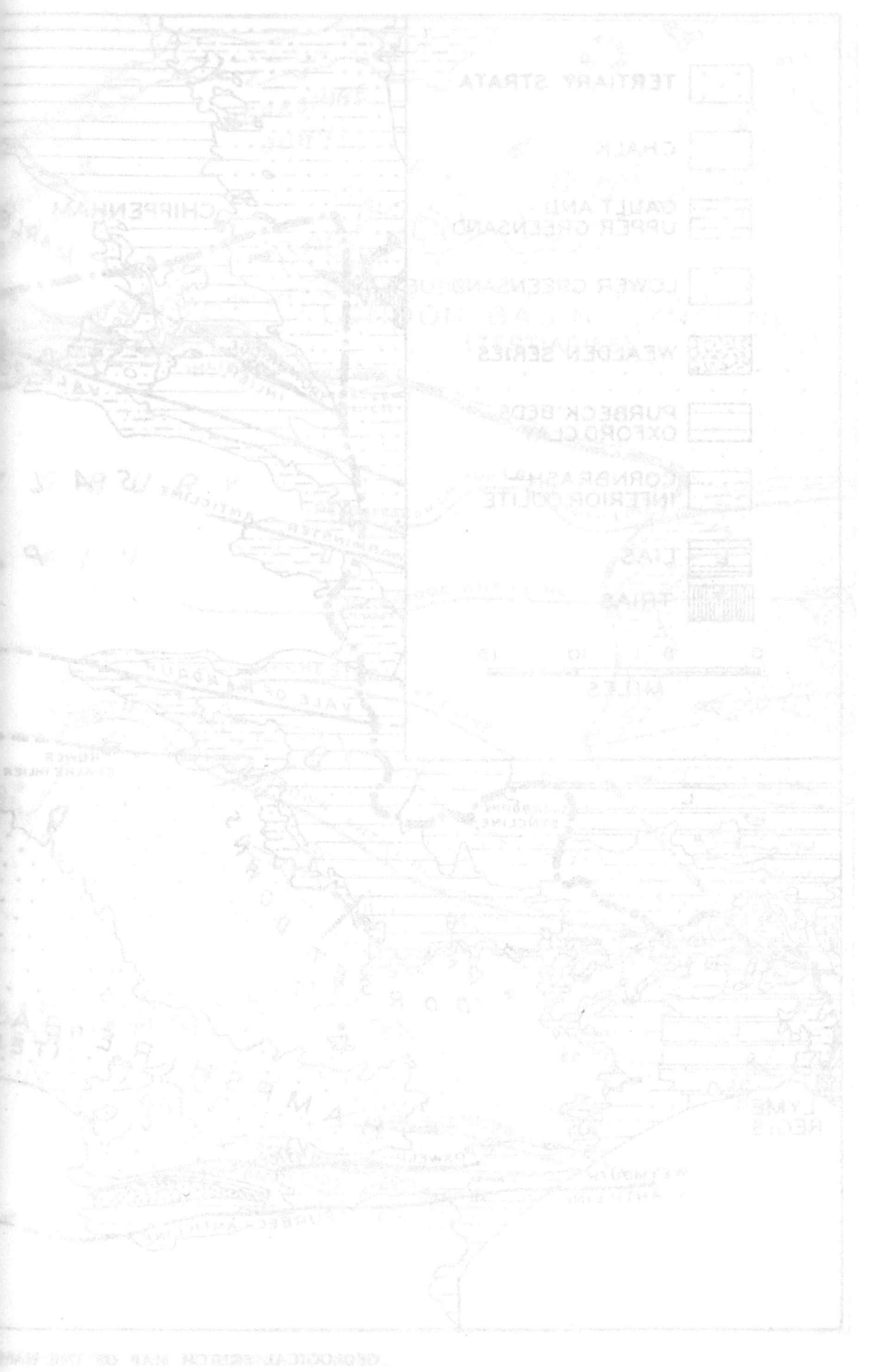

THE HAMPSHIRE BASIN AND ADJOINING AREAS

I. INTRODUCTION

FOR THE PURPOSE of illustrating the geology of Great Britain in the Museum of the Geological Survey the country has been divided into a number of regions. To each of these regions one bay in the Museum has been allotted, and a representative series of specimens, photographs and maps displayed. So far as possible the regions were based on natural divisions, but arbitrary boundaries were obviously necessary on account of limitations of space. Thus the area known as the Hampshire Basin, although naturally divided from the Weald, was extended westwards and northwards to the boundaries fixed for adjoining regions. This area thus includes the whole of Dorset, the greater part of Wiltshire and Hampshire, and the Isle of Wight (Plate I). In this region are exposed all the formations in the Jurassic, Cretaceous, Eocene and Oligocene Systems, as well as a variety of Superficial deposits.

In conformity with the treatment of material in the Museum cases, which is explained by labels appropriate for the general enquirer, this Handbook is designed to explain the geology of the country of which the Museum exhibits are illustrative. The Handbook is prepared for the general reader; detailed and technical accounts are included in the Memoirs of the Geological Survey, which cover most of the region.

From the earliest days of geological investigation the area under consideration has been an attractive field; the pleasing scenery, the number of holiday resorts, the economic value of many of the strata and the scientific interest of the abundant fossils have all been contributing factors in the advance of our knowledge. Thus the presence of high-class building-stone in Portland caused extensive quarrying, in the process of which much material was unearthed and many embedded fossils disclosed. These have long been familiar objects in museums and in local rockeries in the Portland area, and have been described and illustrated in scientific publications. For many generations the popular seaside resorts have attracted visitors whose attention has been drawn to the strata that are readily accessible in the cliffs. In this way large numbers of rock-specimens and fossils have been collected, and many new to science have been duly made known in scientific literature. Famous holiday centres such as Lyme Regis, Weymouth, Swanage and Bournemouth are places well known for their geological importance, while less-frequented localities such as Ringstead Bay, Kimmeridge Bay, Durlston Bay and Hordle Cliffs, Hamstead Cliff, Alum Bay and Atherfield are equally familiar to the geologist.

A small part of the area, a little tract on the Wiltshire border near Bath, is of historic interest since it figures in the oldest geological map—that of the neighbourhood of Bath, published in 1799 by William Smith, the 'Father of English Geology.' In the early part of last century pioneers like De la Beche, Buckland and Conybeare were investigating the strata of the Dorset coast, and making known the remarkable fossils found there.

The abundance of fossils in the cliffs near Lyme Regis has long made that locality familiar to visitors to museums. Here Richard Anning, a cabinet-maker of that town, was among the first to collect and sell fossils; his daughter Mary, born just before the end of the eighteenth century, became famous for her work in collecting and developing the remains of saurian reptiles in the Lias. These were afterwards studied by Owen and other anatomists. Mary Anning discovered the first complete skeleton of *Ichthyosaurus* recorded in this country, also a new saurian reptile that is now the well-known *Plesiosaurus*, and the remains of a flying reptile. Ammonites are found very commonly in the rocks near Lyme Regis, and many species from this locality were described by James Sowerby and James de Carle Sowerby in the 'Mineral Conchology' more than 100 years ago. In the second half of last century (1878-86) the Lias Ammonites were the subject of a monograph, published by the Palaeontographical Society, by Thomas Wright, a Cheltenham surgeon. In recent years detailed examination of the cliffs near Lyme Regis and Charmouth by Dr. W. D. Lang has provided some of the most exact results obtainable by modern methods in the study of fossils, and geological literature has been enriched by a series of contributions by Dr. Lang describing the geology of this neighbourhood. The beds of Inferior Oolite in Dorset have been the subject of work of the first importance in the science of stratigraphy: they were studied intensively by S. S. Buckman, who firmly established the value of ammonites in determining, with relative precision, the geological ages of minor subdivisions of strata, and made interesting deductions as to the conditions under which the beds were deposited.

The cliff-sections in Durlston Bay have also yielded material of classic importance: here Edward Forbes in 1850 worked out the succession of beds and the fossils of the Purbeck formation. Similarly the plant-remains found in the pipe-clay in the cliffs near Bournemouth and in Alum Bay were long ago studied by the palaeobotanists Ettingshausen and Starkie Gardner, with most interesting results; while in recent years critical work by the late Mrs. E. M. Reid and Miss M. Chandler on the plant-remains of the Tertiary beds has added much to our knowledge of the botanical and geological conditions of former times. Beds of several ages in the Isle of Wight are well exposed in cliff-sections; these have afforded a wealth of material that has formed the basis of substantial contributions to geological science. Among the best known are the Wealden beds, with their reptilian remains, and the Oligocene formations, which have yielded large numbers of vertebrates, plants and shells.

The Jurassic and Cretaceous strata of the area have been described systematically in publications of the Geological Survey, but much detailed work on the subdivision of strata by means of fossils has been done since the publication of the volumes on the Jurassic rocks. A comprehensive account of this system by W. J. Arkell, ('The Jurassic System in Great Britain,' Oxford University Press, 1933) gave a great impetus to the study of these strata. Arkell's detailed and well-illustrated descriptions of the Corallian Beds of Dorset appeared in the Proceedings of the Dorset Natural History and Archaeological Society in 1936; and his monographs of the Corallian Lamellibranchs and the Corallian Ammonites have been published by the

Palaeontographical Society. In 1936 the latter Society also published a monograph, by Dr. Helen Muir-Wood, of the Brachiopoda of the Fuller's Earth, which has not only proved useful in determining horizons within this formation but also includes important details of the internal structure as well as the external morphology of this group of fossils. Considerable addition to our knowledge of the Gault and Upper Greensand has also been made by independent investigators since the publication of the first volume of the Survey's Memoirs on the Cretaceous Rocks. The results of these investigations are included in the Monograph of the Gault Ammonites by L. F. Spath, published by the Palaeontographical Society, and in a series of papers by Dr. R. Casey.

The Chalk occupies the greater part of the area included with the Hampshire Basin. Subdivision of this formation in England by means of fossils was first accomplished by Professor Charles Barrois, of Lille, who showed that the same zones established in France could be traced through England. Subsequently the Middle and Upper Chalk of the Dorset Coast and of the Isle of Wight were studied in full detail by A. W. Rowe and C. D. Sherborn, whose work was accompanied by admirable photographs of the coast-sections. The Chalk of Hampshire has been dealt with on a zonal basis by C. Griffith and R. M. Brydone, in books published in 1911 and 1912. The interesting problem of the origin of the Chalk, on which different opinions have been held, has been discussed recently by Mr. Maurice Black (Abstract, Geological Society, 1953).

The Tertiary strata of the Hampshire Basin are well known for the profusion of their fossils. These strata, their classification and natural history have received attention from numerous investigators from the time of Thomas Webster (1814). The posthumous memoir by Edward Forbes (1856) ' On the Tertiary Fluvio-Marine Formation of the Isle of Wight ' (completed by Godwin-Austen, Ramsay and Bristow) is a classic. Later contributions of similar importance were those by J. Starkie Gardner on the Bournemouth Beds and by Gardner, Keeping, and Monckton on the Barton and Bagshot Beds. A useful summary of the Tertiary strata as they occur in the Isle of Wight, where all the divisions in the Hampshire Basin are represented, is included in H. J. Osborne White's ' Short Account of the Geology of the Isle of Wight,' mentioned in the List of Geological Survey Publications. In more recent years considerable additions have been made to our knowledge of the Tertiary strata and fossils. Among the contributions may be mentioned those by Mr. E. St. John Burton (Barton Beds), Mr. Dennis Curry (Eocene stratigraphy and *Nummulites*) and Mr. G. F. Elliott (London Clay palaeogeography). A large amount of detailed work on the Tertiary stratigraphy and palaeontology was accomplished by the late A. G. Davis and A. Wrigley.

Superficial deposits cover a large part of the area and have been investigated by many observers; the presence in many of the gravels of the flint implements of Palaeolithic Man has added much to their interest. In the list of early workers are the well-known names of Lyell, Prestwich, Forbes and John Evans. In 1870 Thomas Codrington published his account of the Superficial Deposits of the South of Hampshire and the Isle of Wight, while in later years the researches of Clement Reid, W. T. Ord, H. Bury, Lt.-Col. J. H. Cooke, Professor L. S. Palmer and H. J. Osborne White were added. The Raised Beach at Portland and the interesting Chesil Bank have been studied by Mr. D. F. W. Baden-Powell, and the latter more recently by Mr. W. V. Lewis. A modern description of the coast of this area is included in ' The Coastline of England and Wales ' (Cambridge University Press, 1946), by Professor J. A. Steers.

Results of studies in local geology have been published from time to time in the Proceedings of the Geologists' Association, in the Proceedings of the Dorset Natural History and Archaeological Society, in the Papers and Proceedings of the Hampshire Field Club and Archaeological Society and in the Proceedings of the Isle of Wight Natural History and Archaeological Society; and an important review, by W. J. Arkell, of the contributions to Dorset geology from 1930-1940, appeared in the journal of the first-named society in 1940. Mention should also be made of ' The Dorset Coast, a Geological Guide,' by Mr. G. M. Davies, 1935.

A list of publications of the Geological Survey dealing with this area, most of which include full bibliographies, is to be found on p. 98. These works, and those of the other authors named, have been freely used in the preparation of this Handbook.

The illustrations of fossils in this Handbook are mostly the work of Miss O. F. Tassart; some were drawn by Mr. R. H. Lennie, and the Ostracods by Dr. F. W. Anderson. Some of the Purbeck fossils were drawn by the late Dr. Arkell for the Memoir on the Weymouth District.

The formations present in the Hampshire Basin and adjoining areas are set out in order below:—

	Superficial deposits
Recent:	Blown Sand and Shingle Beaches
	Alluvium; Tufa; Peat
Pleistocene:	Raised Beach
	River Terraces (Gravels)
	Coombe Deposit
	Angular Flint Gravel
	Plateau Gravel and Brickearth
	Clay-with-flints
	Solid formations
Oligocene:	Hamstead Beds
	Bembridge Beds
	Osborne Beds
	Headon Beds
Eocene:	Barton Beds
	Bracklesham Beds
	Bagshot Beds
	London Clay
	Reading Beds
Cretaceous:	Chalk
	Upper Greensand and Gault
	Lower Greensand
	Wealden
Jurassic:	Purbeck Beds
	Portland Beds
	Kimmeridge Clay
	Corallian Beds
	Oxford Clay and Kellaways Beds
	Cornbrash
	Great Oolite Series
	Inferior Oolite
	Lias

II. JURASSIC STRATA

LIAS

THE OLDEST STRATIFIED rocks that crop out in this region belong to the Lias formation. This formation (its name probably came from the Gaelic word *leac*, a flat stone, see Pl. II B) consists largely of clays and limestones but includes also beds of shale, layers of cement-stones and beds of sand and sandstone. Fossils are commonly found in the Lias, and show that the formation originated as a sea-deposit; remains of saurian reptiles and of insects indicate that the sea was comparatively shallow and that land was not far distant. From a study of the present distribution of the Lias, of the indications of its shore deposits and of the position of older rock-masses it is possible to reconstruct the main outlines of the geography at the time when the strata were deposited. The greater part of what is now England was then under the sea. Parts of an ancient land-mass stood where now we see Cornwall, part of Devon, and most of Wales. The eastern Mendips stood up as islands or shoals in this ancient sea, of which a narrow arm extended over the Bristol Channel and left traces of its shore line near the coast of South Wales. The land mass extended southwards, westwards over Ireland and northwards over most of Scotland, while the sea extended southwards over the area of the present English Channel and as a narrow arm stretched across north-eastern Ireland and over the Hebrides. A further land-mass stood up over the area from East Anglia to London and Kent, extending eastwards. Into this sea rivers carried their burden of sediments, which were spread over its floor; and after chemical and physical changes these became stratified rocks.

In our area the Lias formation crops out only in Dorset. It extends over a small tract from Lyme Regis to near Bridport and northwards to near Beaminster, thence westwards and northwards to the Somerset border in which area is included the Vale of Marshwood, lying mostly on the lower beds of the Lias. A further small outcrop occurs north-west of Sherborne. The cliffs between Lyme Regis and Bridport Harbour (Pl. II A and Figs. 1 and 2) expose some of the finest sections of Lias in England, and the thickness of the formation in this part of Dorset is more than 800 feet. On account of the general dip of the strata towards the east most of the beds can be seen along the coast.

For the purpose of broad comparison throughout the country the Lias is considered under three main divisions, Lower, Middle and Upper. It is also subdivided into stages, or groups of strata characterized by the fossils found in them, and named after the place where they are best developed. Further subdivision has produced a number of zones, or thicknesses of strata characterized by assemblages of fossils and named after one species chosen as an index-fossil. The abundance of fossils, particularly ammonites, in the Lias has enabled palaeontologists to effect the most refined subdivisions. For the purpose of ready recognition in the field the terms here used relate to the local divisions of strata in the respective formations.

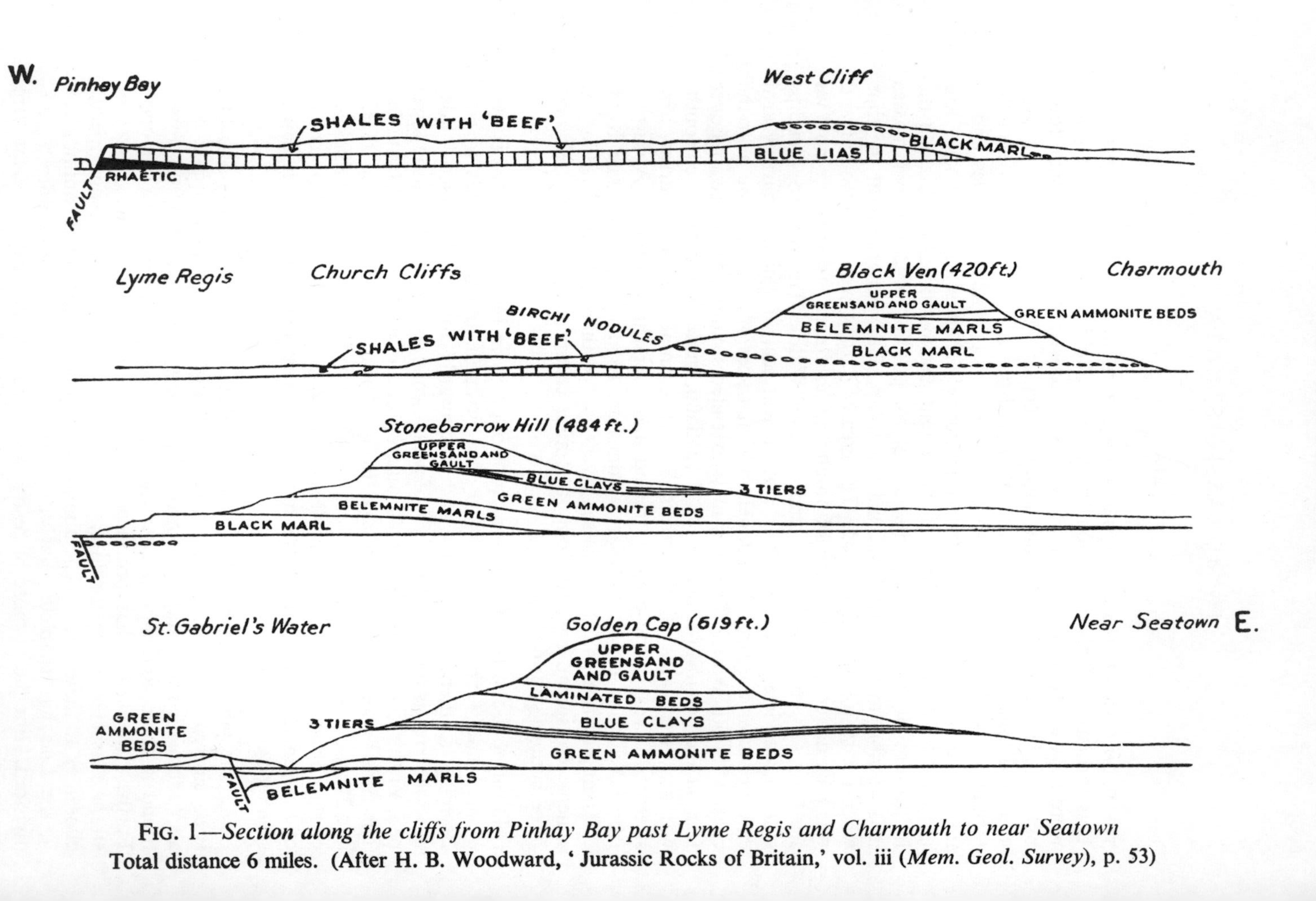

FIG. 1—*Section along the cliffs from Pinhay Bay past Lyme Regis and Charmouth to near Seatown*
Total distance 6 miles. (After H. B. Woodward, ' Jurassic Rocks of Britain,' vol. iii (*Mem. Geol. Survey*), p. 53)

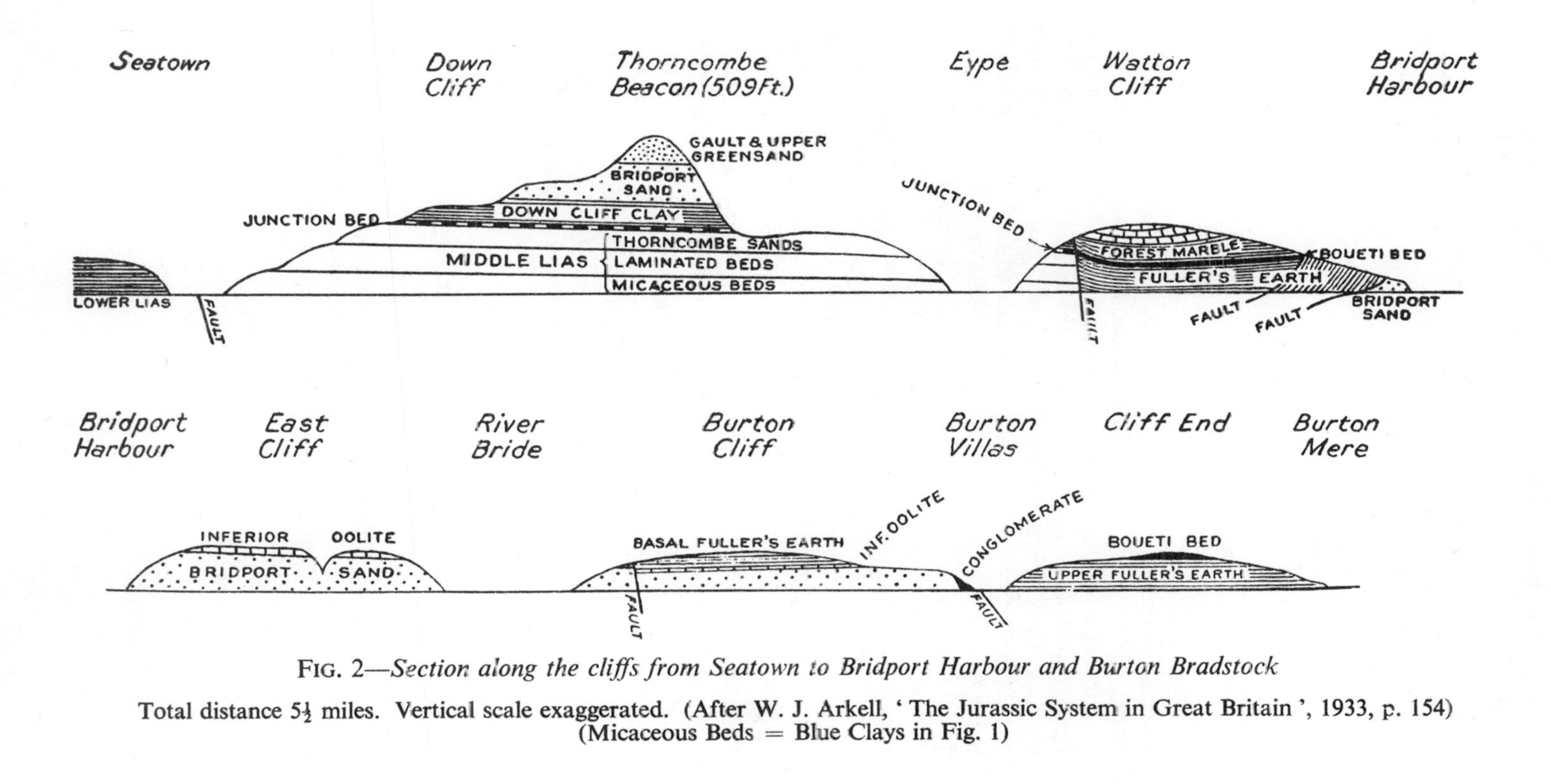

FIG. 2—*Section along the cliffs from Seatown to Bridport Harbour and Burton Bradstock*

Total distance 5½ miles. Vertical scale exaggerated. (After W. J. Arkell, 'The Jurassic System in Great Britain', 1933, p. 154) (Micaceous Beds = Blue Clays in Fig. 1)

Lower Lias.—The Lower Lias is divisible into five principal groups of beds, as follows:—

		Ft
(At the top)	Wear Cliff or Green Ammonite Beds Bluish-grey clays	105
	Stonebarrow or Belemnite Beds Pale grey marls	75
	Black Ven Marls or Black Marl Dark shales and cement-stones	150
	Lower Black Ven Beds or Shales-with-Beef Shales with seams of fibrous calcite	70
	Lyme Regis Beds or Blue Lias Limestones and shales	105

The Blue Lias comprises beds of limestone, shales and marls, with occasional veins of iron pyrites, layers of lignite and thin seams of ' beef ' (fibrous calcite, *i.e.*, calcium carbonate). Near the top of the division are a Fish Bed and a Saurian Bed; and the upper limit of the Blue Lias is marked by the Hard Marl, or Table Ledge (3 ft 6 in.), seen at Lyme Regis in West Cliff, above the Esplanade, in Gun Cliff, and in Church Cliffs; it descends to the beach at the foot of Black Ven. Among the fossils may be noted the oyster-like *Gryphaea arcuata*, popularly known as the ' Devil's Toenail,' the large, smooth bivalve *Lima* (*Plagiostoma*) *gigantea* and the Sea-lily *Isocrinus basaltiformis*. Remains (usually detached vertebrae) of the saurians *Ichthyosaurus* and *Plesiosaurus* and bones of Pterodactyls have also been found. Some layers are crowded with shells of the small brachiopod *Calcirhynchia calcarea*. The Blue Lias is the source of the ammonite-species *Schlotheimia angulata*, *Arietites bucklandi* and *Arnioceras semicostatum*.

The Shales-with-Beef consist of 70 ft of shales, paper-shales, marls, bands of limestone and nodule-beds, and numerous seams of fibrous calcite (' beef ') varying in thickness from one-sixteenth of an inch to four inches. The seams of ' beef ' are cross-fibred and exhibit an interesting cone-in-cone structure, which increases in complexity with the thickness of the seam. The veins have a marly parting between the upper and lower surfaces and although the fibres are terminated by the parting the cones extend through it. Fossils are frequent in this division, ammonites being the commonest, but not well preserved. Among the ammonite genera *Arnioceras* is the most abundant, and ranges from the beds below; *Arietites* and *Cymbites* range into higher beds, while *Megarietites* is restricted to the Shales-with-Beef.

The Black Marl is well seen in the cliff at Black Ven, to the east of Lyme Regis. The beds consist of dark shales, marls and clays, with layers of impersistent limestone and cement-stones. The lowest of the cement-stone layers is the prominent band of Firestone Nodules or *birchi* Bed, so named from the species of ammonite commonly found in it. Near the top of this division is the Coin Stone Bed, or Coin Stone Ledge; farther down is the well-known Pentacrinite Bed, which has yielded many slabs covered with *Pentacrinus briareus*, usually replaced by iron pyrites; and then a lenticular bed of Ammonite Marble. From the Black Marl Beds come the common ammonites *Microderoceras birchi*, *Caenisites brooki*, *Promicroceras planicosta*, *Echioceras raricostatum*, and *Asteroceras stellare*.

The next higher division—the Stonebarrow or Belemnite Beds—appears as a well-marked light-grey band in the higher part of the clay cliffs at Black Ven, on Stonebarrow, and on the foreshore below Golden Cap. It includes marls, shales, and marly limestones; lignite and iron pyrites occur in places. At the top of these beds is an easily recognized thin stone bed, called the Belemnite Stone by reason of the abundance of the pencil-like belemnites seen in it. Fossils, particularly belemnites, are also common in the greyish-black marls beneath the Belemnite Stone.

Above the Belemnite Beds, seen in the cliffs from the eastern side of Black Ven to the base of Golden Cap, are the Green Ammonite (or Wear Cliff) Beds. These consist of bluish-grey marly clays with occasional indurated bands, nodules of hard grey limestone and ferruginous layers. They take their name from the occurrence in them of ammonites (*Androgynoceras lataecosta*) with chambers filled with crystalline calcite of a green colour. The most common ammonites found in these beds are species of *Liparoceras* and *Tragophylloceras loscombi*.

Middle Lias.—In the cliffs farther eastwards from Lyme Regis, on the eastern side of Stonebarrow, on Golden Cap and on Thorncombe Beacon, are exposures of the Middle Lias. About the base of this division, well seen beneath Golden Cap, are thick bands of calcareous sandstone, known as the ' Three Tiers.' Standing out prominently above the Green Ammonite Beds, they form (on Golden Cap) great buttresses along the lower portions of the cliffs. Their total thickness of 35 ft is succeeded by 155 ft of bluish-grey marl and clay, the Micaceous Beds, above which is the ' Starfish ' Bed (4 ft 6 in.), a hard greenish-grey, micaceous sandstone, wherein the complete skeletons of the brittle-star *Ophioderma* are found (Fig. 3).

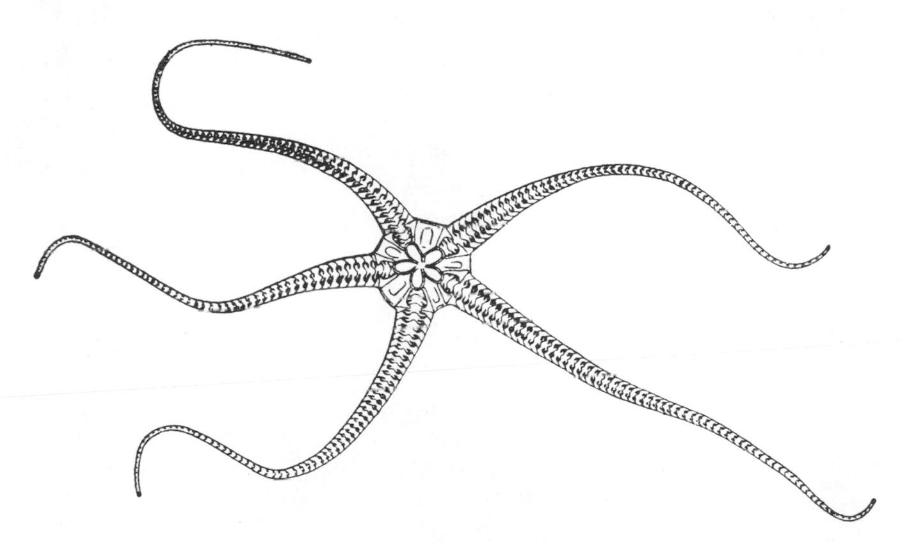

FIG. 3.—*A brittle-star from the ' Starfish ' Bed, Middle Lias* (Ophioderma egertoni *Broderip*)

Next in upward order of succession are the Laminated Beds or Down Cliff Sands (75 ft), which consist of blue, brown and grey micaceous sands,

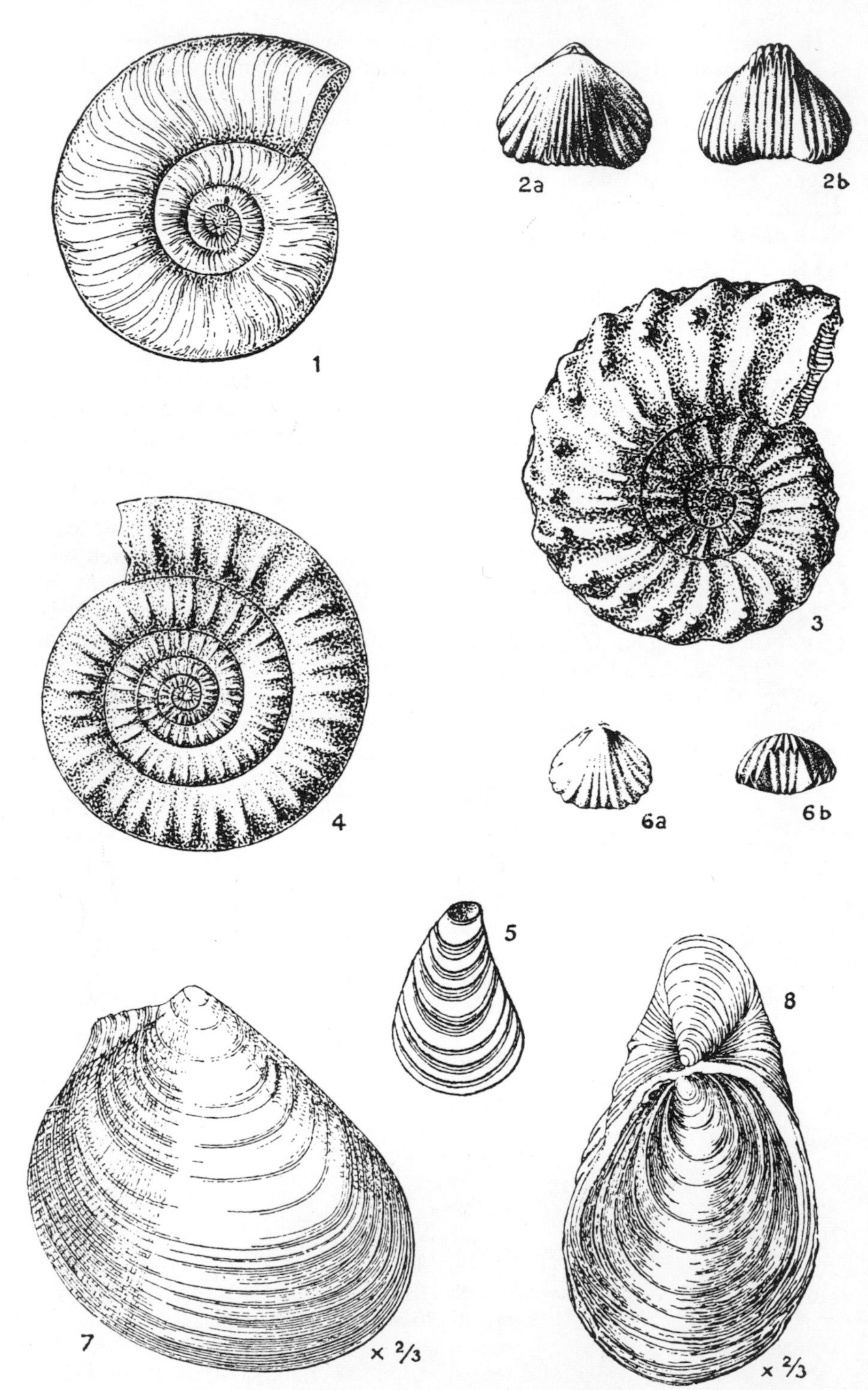

FIG. 4.—*Fossils from the Lias*

clays and marls with ferruginous layers, bands of sandstone and occasional ironstone nodules. Here occur the large oyster-like *Gryphaea cymbium* and *Pseudopecten aequivalvis*.

The Down Cliff Sands are succeeded by an easily recognised bed of hard, sandy limestone; this bed is very fossiliferous and contains, in addition to the fossils just mentioned, several gastropod shells and species of the ammonite *Amaltheus*, particularly *A. margaritatus*, from which it derives its name, the *margaritatus* Bed. This ammonite is not restricted to the *margaritatus* Bed, but ranges up to clays beneath the Marlstone. Another series of sandy beds (35 to 75 ft) lie above this bed, and are called the Thorncombe Sands. These are yellow and light brown sands with large ' doggers ' (indurated masses of sandstone) in the middle; these yield the ammonite *Pleuroceras spinatum* and shells of the brachiopod *Gibbirhynchia thorncombiensis*. Marking the top of the Middle Lias is the Marlstone, a bed of greenish-grey limestone, only 8 inches in thickness on the coast but thicker and highly fossiliferous inland. Among the fossils the brachiopod *Tetrarhynchia tetrahedra* is characteristic.

The Upper Lias.—A peculiar junction bed (2½ to 4½ ft) marks the division between the Middle and Upper Lias; and in this bed are fossils (mostly rolled or worn) of four different ages. The lowest layer contains ammonites of the topmost zone of the Middle Lias; the other layers include ammonites of Upper Lias age; and the various layers separate along planes which were obviously scoured by the sea before the deposition of the next layer. Not only do the fossils show evidence of marine erosion (some of them being cleanly cut through) but the vertical range of the species as known elsewhere shows that a long time was occupied by the deposition of the bed, although its thickness is inconsiderable.

The Junction Bed is exposed on the coast at the top of Down Cliff, along the face of Thorncombe Beacon and for a short distance on Watton Cliff, where it is cut off by a fault. It can also be traced inland.

Above the Junction Bed is the Down Cliff Clay (70 ft), a blue-grey clay, sandy in the upper part. The age of the fossils in the lower part of this clay and the sea-scoured surface of the Junction Bed on which it rests indicate that a long period of erosion intervened before it was deposited. The Down Cliff Clay contains several species of the ammonite *Dumortieria*.

Resting on the Down Cliff Clay is a thickness of 140 ft of bright yellow sands with layers of concretionary sandstone. These beds, known as the Bridport Sands, form the prominent cliffs near Bridport Harbour and at Burton Bradstock; the vertical line of these cliffs is notable, and the beds of sandstone standing out as conspicuous layers in the soft sands present a striking appearance (Pl. III A). Brachiopods and ammonites (among them

---

FIG. 4.—*Fossils from the Lias.*

1. *Dumortieria moorei* (Lycett); 2, a, b. *Tetrarhynchia tetrahedra* (J. Sowerby); 3. *Pleuroceras spinatum* (Bruguière); 4. *Echioceras raricostatum* (Zieten); 5. *Liostrea hisingeri* (Nilsson) [=*Ostrea liassica* Strickland]; 6. *Calcirhynchia calcarea* S. Buckman; 7. *Lima* (*Plagiostoma*) *gigantea* J. Sowerby (× ⅔); 8. *Gryphaea arcuata* Larmack (× ⅔).

species of the *Pleydellia aalensis* type) are found in these sands, and the age of the fossils shows that the upper part of the sands was deposited in the period that followed Upper Lias times, being represented elsewhere by beds of Inferior Oolite.

At Halfway House, between Yeovil and Sherborne, the sandy beds of the Upper Lias are known as the Yeovil Sands, and the Upper Lias here includes the Dew Bed, a hard, shelly, sandy limestone. The Yeovil Sands, with the Dew Bed, are the approximate equivalent of the lower part of the Bridport Sands and Down Cliff Clay of the coast.

INFERIOR OOLITE

These beds vary considerably in lithic character, but are mostly oolitic limestone (often ferruginous), sandy oolites, and sandy limestones. Some beds yield good building stones; others provide material for road-metal, stone fences and lime burning.

The term ‘ oolite ’ (Greek, *oon*, an egg) has reference to the nature of the rocks, many of the beds consisting to a large extent of minute spheroidal grains somewhat resembling the roe of a fish. Fossils (mostly ammonites and other molluscan shells and brachiopods) are abundant, and indicate that the beds were formed in a shallow sea. Also, there is evidence that this sea was disturbed by changing currents, caused by earth-movements that produced gentle folding of the sea floor. As a result of the eroding action of the currents the crests of the low folds were worn down and new deposits were laid down on the older members of the series thus bared. In consequence of this action the thickness of the Inferior Oolite varies, while beds originally deposited over wide areas are now present only in certain places. Such local interruptions in the normal succession of beds are known as ‘ non-sequences.’ Three divisions of the Inferior Oolite (Lower, Middle and Upper) are recognized, the division planes between them being marked by the erosion that accompanied widespread transgressions of the sea. In Dorset this formation is thin in comparison with its development in the Cotswolds, but is interesting on account of the abundance of its fossils and the light they throw on the conditions of its deposition. It can be said that the foundations of modern stratigraphy were laid by the study of the intricacies of this formation. Different beds, often very thin, can be recognized by distinctive fossils, but the beds vary from place to place, and detailed description is thus inappropriate here. However, the wealth of detail collected and interpreted by S. S. Buckman and by Linsdall Richardson, and clearly reviewed by W. J. Arkell, enables broad generalizations to be made.

Lower Inferior Oolite.—The basal portion of the Inferior Oolite whether a limestone (i.e. the normal Inferior Oolite facies) or a sandy deposit (as the upper part of the Bridport Sands), generally yields abundant examples of the ammonite *Leioceras opalinum*. The base of the Inferior Oolite in this area, as marked by the normal facies, is a bed named after the zonal ammonite *Tmetoceras scissum*, the *scissum* Bed. Between Burton Bradstock and Crewkerne this is a grey sand-rock not unlike the Bridport Sands, varying in thickness from 1 to 3 feet. In many places this is overlain by the Yellow

A. COAST SCENERY BETWEEN BLACK VEN AND GOLDEN CAP, DORSET

B. CLIFFS OF BLUE LIAS, LYME REGIS
(*For details see p.* iv)

A. CLIFFS OF BRIDPORT SANDS, WEST BAY, DORSET

B. TOPOGRAPHY OF THE AREA BETWEEN ABBOTSBURY AND THE CHESIL BANK
(*For details see p.* iv)

Conglomerate, a thin pebbly layer containing fossils derived from the destruction of other beds, among them the ammonites *Brasilia* and *Graphoceras*, the gastropod shell *Cirrus nodosus* and the bivalved shell *Coelastarte excavata*. North-east and east of Bridport the Lower Inferior Oolite thins out, but expands west of Bridport, and beds representing zonal subdivisions can be recognized.

In the Sherborne district the *scissum* Bed is rarely seen, and the Lower Inferior Oolite is represented by yellow and blue limestone, including a bed known locally as the Paving Bed and a rock full of the shells of the small brachiopod *Homoeorhynchia ringens*.

Middle Inferior Oolite.—This is represented near Burton Bradstock (Fig. 5) by the Red Bed (2 ft 10 in.) consisting of three layers. The bottom layer is of bluish-green limestone with brown ooliths and contains numerous large limonitic concretions called 'snuff-boxes.' The middle layer is of hard crystalline limestone with ironshot ooliths, and the upper layer is also a hard crystalline limestone, grey in colour and containing a large proportion of crinoid-fragments. The surface of the Red Bed shows evidence of erosion; it is waterworn and pitted, and resting on it here and there are patches of conglomerate. This conglomerate is largely made up of constituents of the Red Bed that have been eroded away elsewhere.

Near Sherborne the Middle Inferior Oolite consists, for the most part, of a bed of grey sandy limestone with marly partings; it includes also some Fossil Beds, which, like some of the beds in the lower division, have yielded a number of well-preserved ammonites and gastropods.

Upper Inferior Oolite.—The upper part of the formation differs markedly from the lower and middle divisions; it comprises the deposits of a transgressive sea that swept westwards after the Middle beds had been raised and gently folded by earth-movements and eroded by current-action. It rests, therefore, on different beds in different places and outside our area extends across the edges of the Lias, to rest directly on yet older rocks.

The beds of Upper Inferior Oolite are known as the Top Beds, and are exposed in the cliffs between Bridport Harbour and Burton Bradstock; north of the latter locality they are faulted out, but reappear near Bothenhampton and continue with irregular and faulted outcrop to Beaminster; they are exposed also on Chideock Quarry Hill. They thicken considerably near Sherborne, where they attain a thickness of 45 feet. The bottom zone, named after the ammonite *Strenoceras niortense*, is interesting because of its restricted distribution. Its only occurrence in England is as a thin layer of ironshot oolite in the Sherborne district, while its fossils have been found in a conglomerate on the coast. The explanation of this unusual feature, given by A. Morley Davies, is that the bed is the first deposit of an invading sea and was overlapped by more widely spread deposits as transgression proceeded. Near the coast in Dorset the next bed, named after the ammonite *Garantiana*, is either a thin layer of ferruginous marl or a layer of ironshot limestone; in places, as at Uploders, the marly layer is underlain

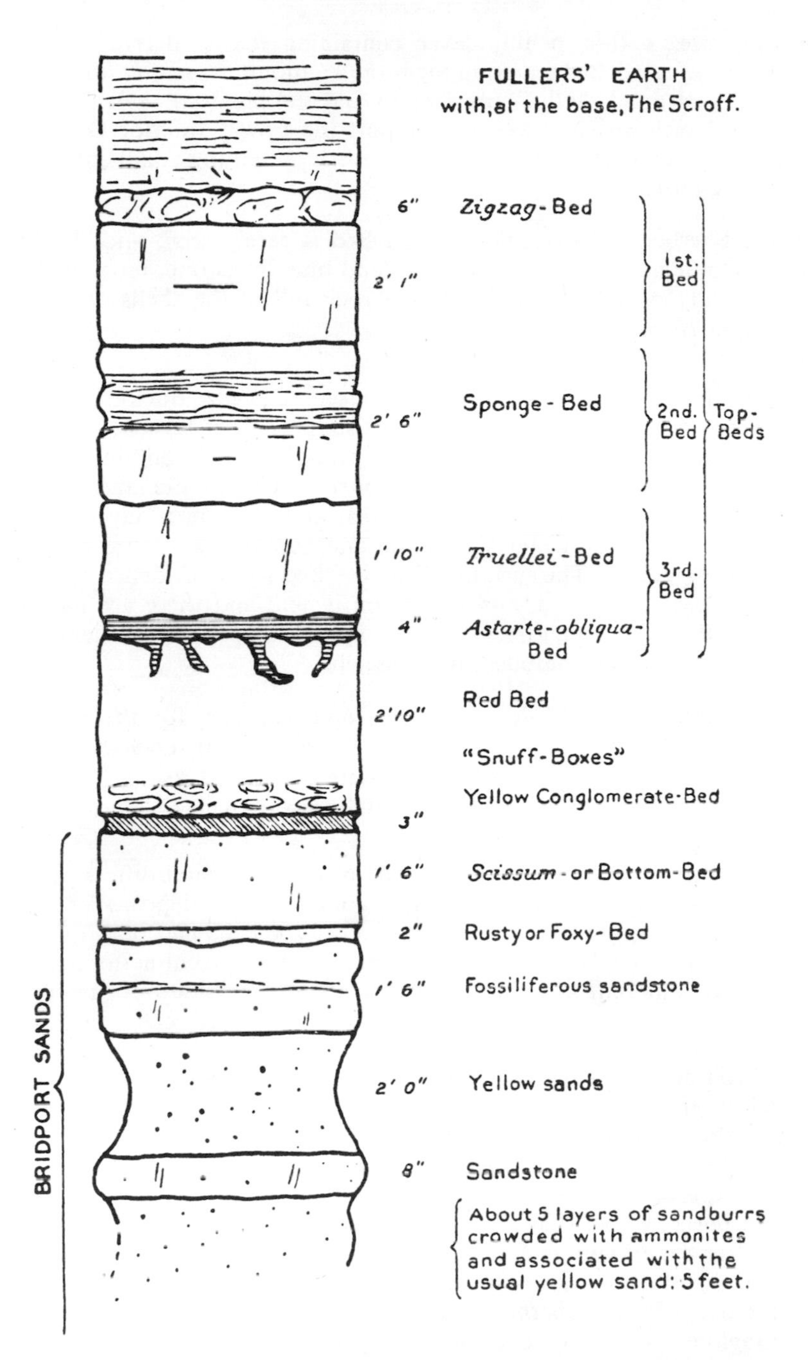

FIG. 5—*Vertical section of the Inferior Oolite and contiguous deposits exposed at Burton Bradstock*

(Adapted from L. Richardson, *Proc. Cotteswold Naturalists' Field Club*, vol. xxiii, pt. i, 1927, p. 60)

by ironshot limestone. Fossils are frequently common in both beds and include many lamellibranchs and gastropods and the belemnite *Belemnopsis bessina*.

The *Garantiana* Bed is also known as the *Astarte obliqua* Bed on account of the frequency of the lamellibranch of that name; it often appears to be joined on to the Red Bed. The next higher division (the Zone of *Strigoceras truelli*) is a bed (1 to 3 ft) of limestone in which, among the fossils, the brachiopod shell *Sphaeroidothyris sphaeroidalis* is particularly common. The uppermost subdivision of the Upper Inferior Oolite is the zone of *Parkinsonia schloenbachi*. This includes beds of limestone, massive and poorly fossiliferous in the lower part and marly and crowded with sponges and small organisms (microzoa) in the upper part. This varies in thickness from 4½ ft at Burton Bradstock to 14 ft at Chideock. In the Sherborne district the Top Beds include the Sherborne Building Stone (10 to 20 ft) and the Rubbly Limestone Beds (12 to 21 ft).

GREAT OOLITE SERIES

The Great Oolite Series was named after the most distinctive member, a massive oolitic limestone which is of considerable thickness near Bath, where it has been extensively quarried as a building-stone. Included also in the series are beds of entirely different character, such as clays, marls, sands and shelly limestone. All these beds are of marine origin, and illustrate the striking fact that beds laid down at approximately the same time differ in lithology within comparatively short distances. On account of the variability of these strata, it is customary to group them as a series; the base rests quite conformably on the Inferior Oolite. The fossils preserved in these beds differ in their assemblages, as do the deposits in lithic character. Ammonites, which are common throughout the Inferior Oolite and are accurate guides to the numerous subdivisions of this formation, are less constant in occurrence in the Great Oolite Series. Other fossils of the Great Oolite are associated with the facies of the deposit, and differ accordingly in various parts of the country. Consequently, detailed subdivision of the series based on the occurrence of species of ammonites is not possible. We have instead to consider the members of the series as they occur locally. Among the fossils, shells of brachiopods are abundant, and although they do not occur evenly over wide areas they have been found very useful in the determination of horizons.

On the Dorset coast these beds are seen faulted between the Middle Lias and the Bridport Sands at Watton Cliff (west of Bridport Harbour); they appear again to the east, at Burton Cliff (Fig. 2). Inland the outcrop, of variable width, borders that of the Inferior Oolite and extends from the coast northwards past Beaminster and thence past the county boundary near Mosterton; the county boundary lies along the outcrop as far as Stalbridge, a small area of Lias and Inferior Oolite intervening around Sherborne. In Wiltshire the outcrop runs along the county boundary from near Winkfield, south of Bradford-on-Avon, northwards and out of the area. A small tract separated from the main outcrop lies near the Fleet, west of Weymouth.

In Dorset the following divisions are recognized:—

Forest Marble
The *boueti* Bed
Upper Fuller's Earth Clay
Fuller's Earth Rock
Lower Fuller's Earth Clay

At the base of the Lower Fuller's Earth are two subordinate beds, seen near the coast; a lower *zigzag* Bed (named after the ammonite *Zigzagiceras zigzag* and included by some authors in the Inferior Oolite), and above it a bed called the Scroff. On the coast the *zigzag* Bed is a white limestone 6 in. in thickness; near Sherborne it is represented by the Crackment limestone (25 to 35 ft). The Scroff is a hardened marl (3 in.). The Lower Fuller's Earth Clay (110 ft on the coast, but thicker inland) is a bluish grey marly clay, laminated and with small nodules of pyrites in the lower part; above are grey and umber-coloured clays. At various localities in Dorset an oyster-bank is seen resting on the *zigzag* Bed. The oysters are small shells with fine ribbing on one valve, and are known as *Liostrea* (*Catinula*) *knorrii*; the bed is called the *knorrii* Bed. Not many fossils have been found in the Lower Fuller's Earth of the area, and of the brachiopods, common higher in the succession, only occasional examples of *Wattonithyris* and *Rhynchonelloidella* have been recorded.

In Dorset the Fuller's Earth Rock forms a distinct surface feature where, with a thickness of 35 ft, it enters the county near Haydon. After some displacement through faulting it reappears in Sherborne Park and extends, becoming thinner, in a south-westerly direction to Beaminster, where it is represented by a line of intermittent nodules. In the neighbourhood of Sherborne the rock is a grey or buff-coloured argillaceous limestone, weathering to a cream colour. Its fossils include numerous Ornithellids and other brachiopods, ammonites (*Tulites*) and lamellibranchs. Near Thornford it yielded *Tulites subcontractus*, *Pholadomya lirata*, *Rhynchonelloidella wattonensis*, *Ornithella bathonica* and other brachiopods. West of Thornford its thickness is reduced, and between Beaminster and the Dorset coast there is no trace of this bed.

Rubbly limestone-beds with brachiopods that occur near the middle of the Fuller's Earth Clay on the coast were formerly thought to represent the Fuller's Earth Rock, but a study of the fossils by Miss Muir-Wood has shown that these beds are different from the true Fuller's Earth Rock to the north. The most common brachiopods are *Wattonithyris wattonensis* and *Rhynchonelloidella wattonensis;* other common forms are *Rugitela bullata*, *Tubithyris powerstockensis*, *Rhynchonelloidella smithi*, and lamellibranchs and gastropods. The ammonite *Morrisiceras* has also been found, but no Ornithellids. The name *wattonensis* Beds has been proposed by Messrs. Kellaway and Vernon Wilson for these beds.

There are thus two developments of rock-beds in the Fuller's Earth Clay in Dorset: the true Fuller's Earth Rock traceable from the north and petering out near Beaminster, and an upper rock-bed, well developed as argillaceous limestone bands with intervening clays on the coast at Eypesmouth and Watton Cliff, and continuing inland, becoming thinner and disappearing near Sherborne Park. The two rock-beds, separated by clay, were interpreted formerly as the Fuller's Earth Rock repeated by a fault between Beer Hackett and Sherborne Park; but more recent work, aided by the study of the fossils, has shown the true relationship of the beds.

The Upper Fuller's Earth Clays, attaining a thickness of more than 100 ft on the coast, are greenish clays with a few stone bands at the top. At the base is a remarkable bed made up almost entirely of shells of the oyster *Liostrea hebridica* (=*O. sowerbyi*), a form long mistaken for *Ostrea acuminata*, an oyster that appeared much earlier. This oyster-bank is well seen on the shore of the Fleet, south of Langton Herring. The Fuller's Earth, as used for commercial purposes, is still mined south of Bath and occurs only in the Upper Fuller's Earth Clay.

A thin but conspicuous layer, the *boueti* Bed (1 ft) rests on the top of the Upper Clays; it is remarkable for the profusion of brachiopod shells (mostly *Goniorhynchia boueti*) that it contains. These are freely strewn on the beach at Herbury, on the shore of the Fleet, and their frequency has enabled the bed to be traced along the coast and inland to past Sherborne. Deposition of sediment was evidently very slow when this bed was formed, for many of its fossils are frequently encrusted with polyzoa, marine worms and tiny oysters. Similar evidence of a pause in deposition is to be seen in the north-western corner of the area, but other conditions are different. Here the top of the Fuller's Earth Clay is represented by beds of oolitic limestone, the Great Oolite. The surface of this limestone was evidently under clear water for a time, for much of it is covered by bases of the stalked ' pear-encrinite ' (*Apiocrinus*), in natural position. Presumably these were killed by mud entering the area, and their remains, with those of other inhabitants of the sea-floor, became freely encrusted with smaller organisms. Renewed sedimentation subsequently caused a clay-bed to be laid down; this is the well-known Bradford Clay, which attains a thickness of 10 ft, and marks the local base of the overlying formation, the Forest Marble.

The term ' Forest Marble ' is used generally to denote a hard, flaggy limestone, usually false-bedded and largely composed of broken shells of oysters and pectens. This rock is a facies-rock, and the conditions under which it was deposited set in earlier in some districts than in others. Hence the name Forest Marble does not denote an exact stratigraphical horizon. The name was applied to beds because they included limestones suitable for being polished as ornamental stones, the forest indicated being that of Wychwood, in Oxfordshire. Arkell gave the name Wychwood Beds to the upper part of the Forest Marble group, and Bradford Beds to the lower.

The Forest Marble beds comprise a mass of limestone with a bed of greenish-brown sandy or micaceous clay above and below. These three divisions are of approximately equal thickness, and the whole is from 80 to 90 ft thick in South Dorset. Near Sherborne the beds increase in thickness to 130 ft, and here the limestone, by reason of its thickness and hardness, forms a prominent feature in the landscape. It has been used locally, for building and road-making; and the upper beds near Sherborne, as also in Wiltshire, include a sandy development, the Hinton Sands.

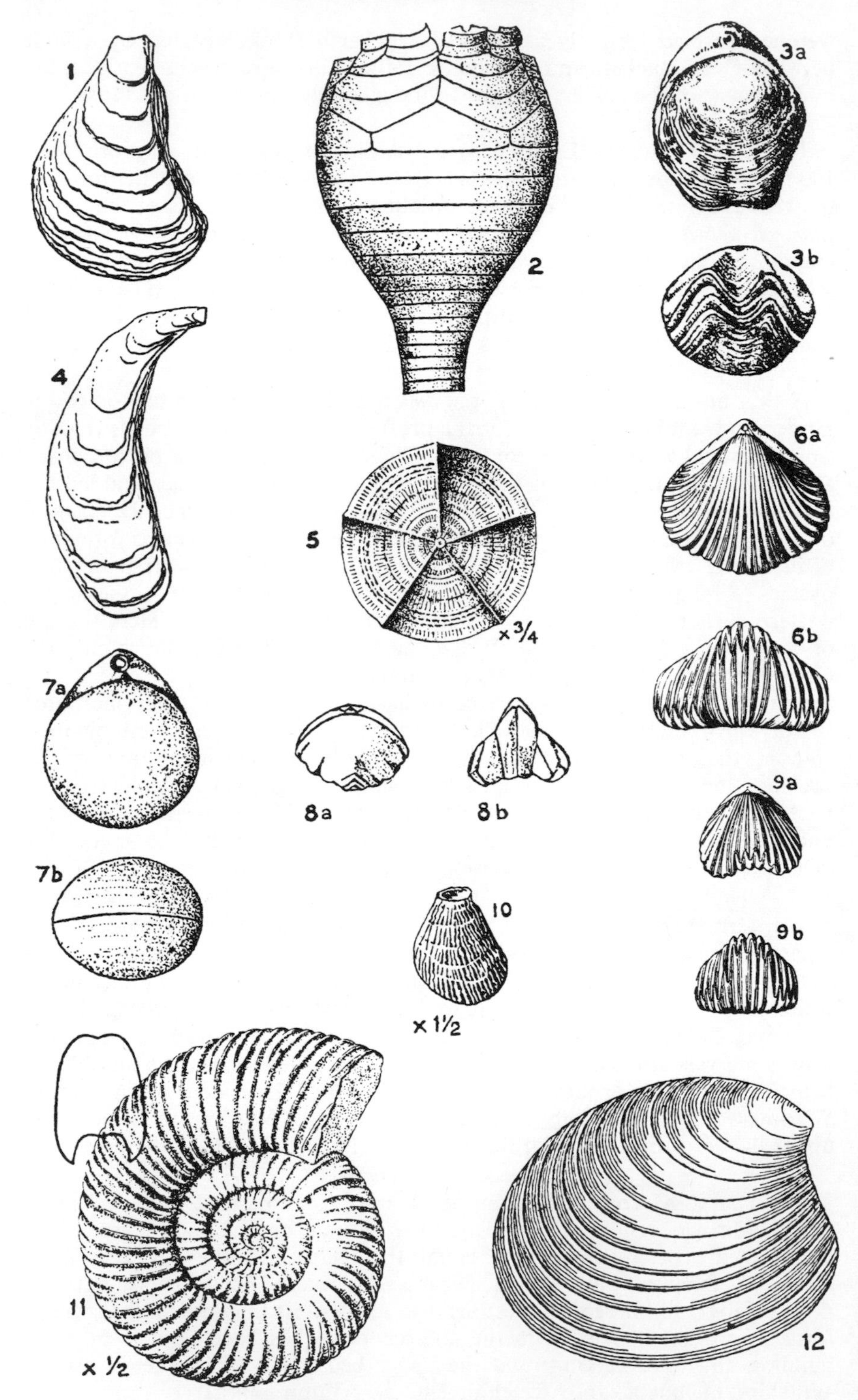

FIG. 6.—*Fossils from the Inferior Oolite and the Great Oolite*

Between the Forest Marble and the Fuller's Earth in Wiltshire is the Great Oolite Limestone division. The disappearance of this limestone a short distance south of Bradford-on-Avon has given rise to some discussion. To the south of Bradford-on-Avon it comprises beds of oolitic freestone and ragstone, and is the source of the famous Bath Stone. This rock, a fine-grained oolite (8 to 30 ft) is mined at Box, Corsham and Bradford. At the base of the limestone series are the Lower Rag Beds (10 to 40 ft) which include limestone and fissile oolite with corals. Above the Freestone beds west of Bradford are the Upper Rag Beds (up to 8 ft), and above these, at Ancliff, is a coarse fossiliferous oolite with numerous small shells. The highest subdivision is the white or cream-coloured oolite (12 to 20 ft), on which at Bradford the Bradford Clay rests. Drifted corals, such as *Isastraea limitata* and *Montlivaltia caryophyllata*, and occasional sponges, are found in a bed, known as the Coral Bed, which forms the lower part of this subdivision.

CORNBRASH

After the last of the varied deposits of the Great Oolite series had been laid down a more widespread change of marine conditions took place and resulted in a general extension and transgression of the sea. The deposits of this sea formed what is known as the Cornbrash, a formation that extends with little interruption from Dorset to Yorkshire. The new conditions did not remain settled for long, for a renewal of transgressive movement took place. As a result two divisions of this formation are recognizable, the Lower and the Upper Cornbrash, which differ in lithology as well as in the fossils that they contain. In places a pebble bed marks the line of juction and the plane of the second transgression.

Although this formation is so constant throughout the country its outcrop is nowhere very wide; the two divisions do not exceed 30 ft in thickness. The name Cornbrash has reference to the agricultural nature of the soil (stony or brashy) to which it often gives rise; but this feature obtains only when it is overlain by clayey or sandy beds. In lithic character the Lower Cornbrash consists chiefly of marly rubble and compact limestone; the Upper Cornbrash includes sandy marl, concretionary limestone and flaggy beds of hard pinkish limestone. Among the fossils the ammonites are distinctive: the thin, laterally-compressed *Clydoniceras* characterizes the Lower division; and the robust, inflated, and plainly-ribbed *Macrocephalites* is restricted to the Upper division. But the most ready means of subdivision is provided by the brachiopods; four zones, two lower and two upper, can be identified by means of these shells. Among the brachiopods are *Cererithyris intermedia*, *Obovothyris obovata* and *Kallirhynchia yaxleyensis* in the Lower Cornbrash and *Microthyridina siddingtonensis*, *M. lagenalis* and *Rhynchonelloidella cerealis* in the Upper division.

FIG. 6.—*Fossils from the Inferior Oolite and the Great Oolite.*

1. *Liostrea hebridica* (Forbes); 2. *Apiocrinus parkinsoni* (Schlotheim); 3, a, b. *Wattonithyris nunneyensis* Muir-Wood; 4. *Liostrea hebridica* (Forbes) var. *elongata* Dutertre; 5. *Apiocrinus* (top joint of stem) (×¾); 6, a, b. *Goniorhynchia boueti* (Davidson); 7, a, b. *Sphaeroidothyris sphaeroidalis* (J. de C. Sowerby); 8, a, b. *Homoeorhynchia ringens* (von Buch); 9, a, b. *Rhynchonelloidella smithi* (Davidson); 10. *Liostrea* (*Catinula*) *knorrii* (Voltz) (×1½); 11. *Parkinsonia parkinsoni* (J. Sowerby) (×½); 12. *Astarte* (*Neocrassina*) *modiolaris* (Lamarck) [=*Astarte obliqua* Deshayes].

Lamellibranchs are commonly found, the small finely-marked *Meleagrinella [Pseudomonotis] echinata* and species of *Astarte* and *Trigonia* characterizing the Lower Cornbrash, while the sharply-folded oyster *Lopha marshii* is typical of the Upper Cornbrash. The echinoid *Nucleolites clunicularis* is also of frequent occurrence.

Some exposures, as at East Chickerell, East Fleet, Yetminster and quarries near Trowbridge, show only Lower Cornbrash; those at Corscombe. Stalbridge and Holwell exhibit both divisions. The most complete section in the area is that on the shore of the Fleet at Abbotsbury Swannery. The outcrop of the Cornbrash is marked by a line of villages, because the porous strata, resting on the impervious Forest Marble clay beneath, yield local supplies of water. Also, coming as it does between two clay formations. its outcrop is usually a prominent ridge of higher ground.

KELLAWAYS BEDS AND OXFORD CLAY

The passage from the uppermost Cornbrash to the succeeding deposit was very gradual, and the bottom bed of this formation, a bed of green, grey or blue clay, 10 to 12 ft in thickness, is known as the Kellaways Clay. This clay takes its name from a village in Wiltshire, just beyond the northern limit of our area. At Kellaways, also, above the clay, are hardened sandy beds which have been called the Kellaways Rock. This sandy development is irregular in extent and varies in thickness from a few feet up to 50 feet. The Kellaways Beds have a distinctive suite of fossils; in the Kellaways Clay are the ammonites *Cadoceras sublaeve* and *Proplanulites koenigi* and the Kellaways Rock yields *Sigaloceras calloviense*. Among other fossils are numerous lamellibranchs, including *Pleuromya*, *Anisocardia*, *Corbula macneillii* and *Gryphaea bilobata*.

The thick and constant Oxford Clay, of which the Kellaways Beds are the basal members, extends continuously, save for the area of the overstep of the Chalk of the Dorset Heights, from the Dorset coast to Yorkshire. Its thickness in the area varies from about 500 ft on the coast to 600 ft in North Wiltshire. In Dorset the Oxford Clay is exposed by the shores of the East Fleet, where the most fossiliferous section is at Tidmoor Point, and in the cliffs north of Weymouth. The best exposure of the Kellaways Rock is in the brickyard to the east of Chickerell, near Weymouth, where sandy beds include characteristic doggers and lenticles of hard sandstone. The oyster-like *Gryphaea bilobata*, typical of this horizon, is particularly common in these beds. The lower beds of the Oxford Clay, also well exposed at Chickerell (in the westerly brickyard) are shaly clays and rusty shales, with crushed ammonites, occasional doggers and septarian nodules. Higher in the sequence the clays are bluish-grey and the fossils pyritized. In the upper part of the series are the Red Nodule Beds, so named from the concretionary

---

FIG. 7.—*Fossils from the Cornbrash and the Oxford Clay.*

1. *Nucleolites clunicularis* (Auctorum); 2. *Quenstedtoceras lamberti* (J. Sowerby); 3. *Microthyridina lagenalis* (Schlotheim); 4. *Cererithyris intermedia* (J. Sowerby); 5. *Kosmoceras duncani* Auctorum; 6, a, b. *Obovothyris obovata* (J. Sowerby); 7. *Meleagrinella [Pseudomonotis] echinata* (W. Smith); 8, a, b. *Rhynchonelloidella cerealis* (S. Buckman); 9. *Microthyridina siddingtonensis* (Walker); 10. *Dicroloma trifidum* (Phillips); 11. *Gryphaea dilatata* J. Sowerby; 12. *Procerithium damonis* (Lycett); 13, a, b. *Nucula menkei* Roemer.

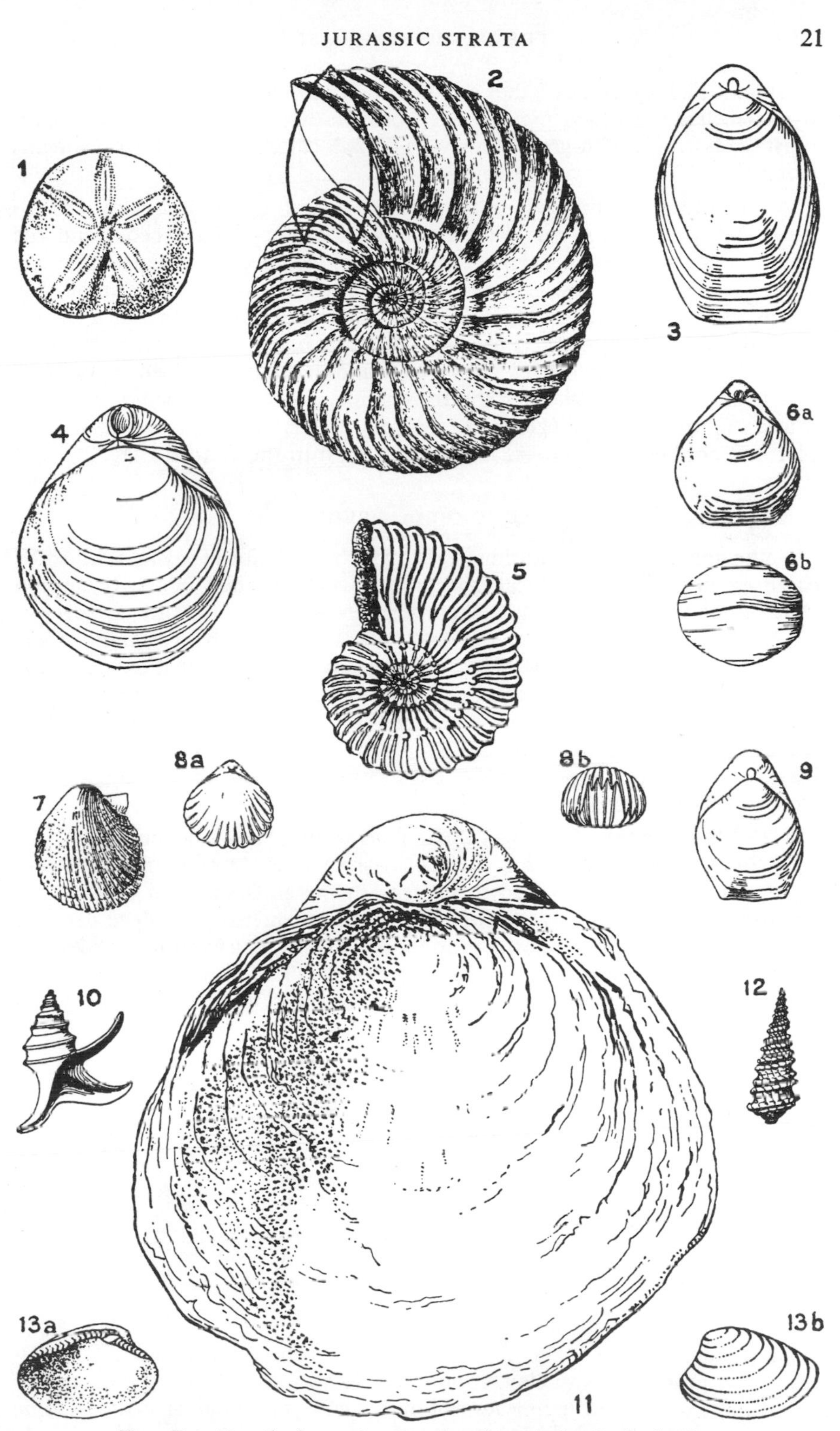

FIG. 7.—*Fossils from the Cornbrash and the Oxford Clay*

nodules (' Kidney Stones ') that are abundant in them. At this horizon large oyster-shells, *Gryphaea dilatata*, are conspicuously common. The uppermost beds are bluish-grey clays with small calcareous nodules (cement-stones).

Ammonites occur throughout the formation, the commonest being *Kosmoceras* and *Quenstedtoceras*, with *Cardioceras* in the highest beds; and the regular and restricted occurrence of the various species provides a means of subdivision into zones. Lamellibranch shells are also numerous among the fossils, gastropods are occasionally found and the clustered tubes of a marine annelid (*Serpula vertebralis*) are of frequent occurrence. The large stout belemnite *Cylindroteuthis puzosiana* is found both in the Kellaways Beds and in the Oxford Clay. Vertebrate remains in the latter include those of saurian reptiles and fish (*Lepidotus*, *Hybodus*, etc.). Crystals of selenite and pieces of coniferous wood are frequently found in the Oxford Clay.

CORALLIAN BEDS

Following the steady conditions under which the Oxford Clay was deposited came certain changes in local geography which resulted in the formation of different kinds of deposits. There were evidently changes in the level of the land and in the depth of the sea, with accompanying variation in the strength of the currents. At times there was considerable shallowing of the sea; corals grew abundantly and in places formed reefs. On account of the frequency of corals in various parts of the formation the name Corallian has been adopted. Early subdivisions of the formation were based on lithology, and comprised upper and lower beds of Calcareous Grit, with Coralline Oolite between.

The full sequence of the Corallian beds, reaching a thickness of about 200 ft, is well exposed on the Dorset coast between Osmington and Ringstead; the succession was also to be seen in the cliffs south of Weymouth, but has since been largely obscured by fortification works. More detailed subdivisions must now be noticed individually since they exhibit considerable differences both in lithology and fossil content. The following is the succession on the coast, most of the beds being named after the places at which they are particularly well developed (Fig. 8):—

(At the top)
Ringstead Coral Bed
Ringstead Waxy Clay
Sandsfoot Grit
Sandsfoot Clay
' *Trigonia* ' *clavellata* Bed
Osmington Oolite
Bencliff Grit
Nothe Clay
' *Trigonia* ' *hudlestoni* Bed
Nothe Grit

As pointed out by Arkell, these beds represent three cycles of deposition, each beginning with clay, continuing with sand and ending with oolitic limestones; and at each limestone phase there was coral growth in some area, though not always in Dorset.

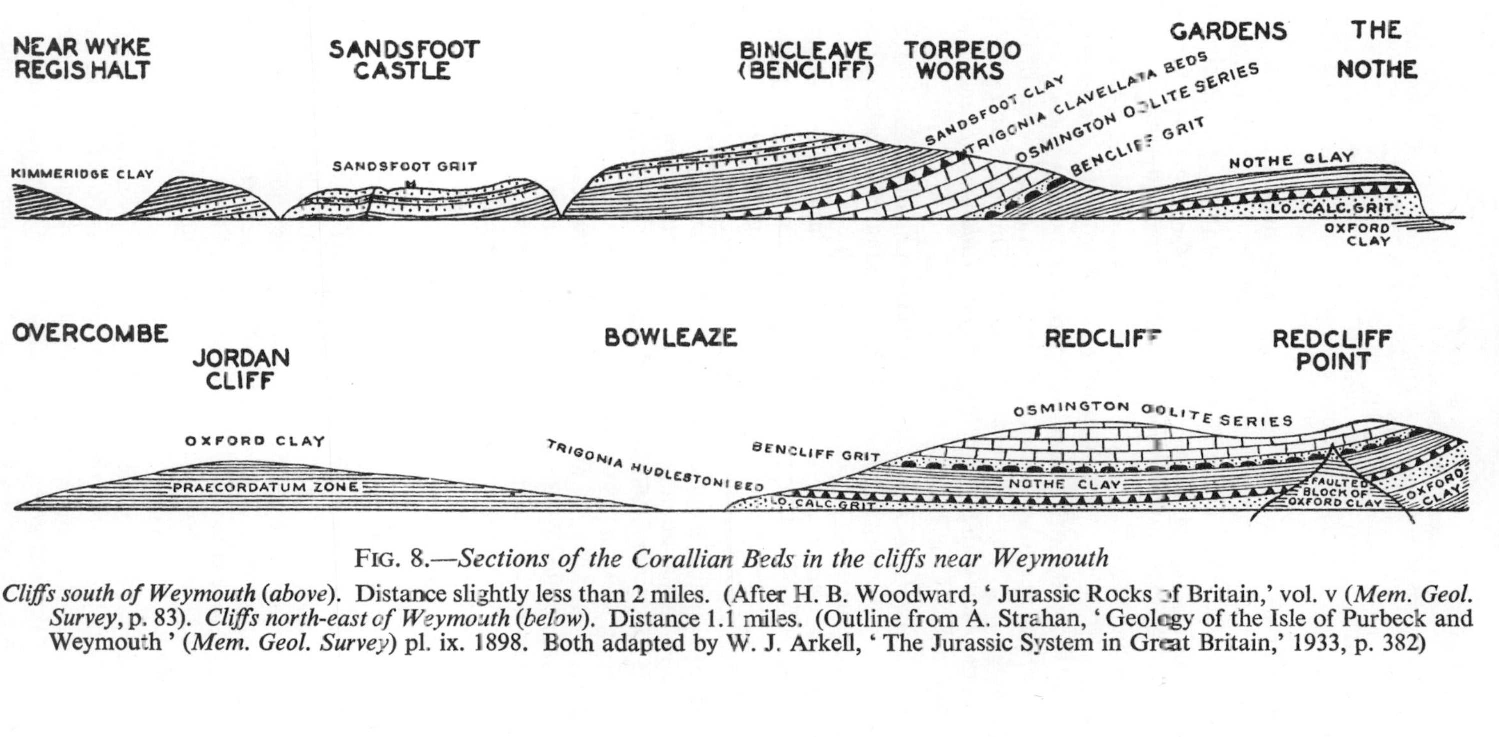

FIG. 8.—*Sections of the Corallian Beds in the cliffs near Weymouth*

Cliffs south of Weymouth (*above*). Distance slightly less than 2 miles. (After H. B. Woodward, ' Jurassic Rocks of Britain,' vol. v (*Mem. Geol. Survey*, p. 83). *Cliffs north-east of Weymouth* (*below*). Distance 1.1 miles. (Outline from A. Strahan, ' Geology of the Isle of Purbeck and Weymouth ' (*Mem. Geol. Survey*) pl. ix. 1898. Both adapted by W. J. Arkell, ' The Jurassic System in Great Britain,' 1933, p. 382)

First Cycle	Second Cycle	Third Cycle
3. '*Trigonia*' *hudlestoni* Limestone (coral reefs in Wiltshire)	3. Osmington Oolite Series and '*Trigonia*' *clavellata* Beds (coral reefs in Wiltshire)	3. Westbury Iron Ore and Ringstead Coral Bed
2. Nothe Grits	2. Bencliff Grit	2. Sandsfoot Grit
1. Oxford Clay	1. Nothe Clay	1. Sandsfoot Clay

The Nothe Grits (12 to 35 ft) are grey, sandy beds with bands of gritstone, some with 'cannon-ball' concretions. Fossils: *Gryphaea dilatata*, *Cardioceras persecans*. The '*Trigonia*' *hudlestoni* Bed (6 ft) is a massive brownish-grey limestone, full of fucoid markings. Highly fossiliferous ('*Trigonia*' *hudlestoni*, *Perisphinctes*, *Cardioceras*, many lamellibranchs).

The Nothe Clay (*Gryphaea dilatata*, etc.) is bluish and sandy, and attains a thickness of 40 feet. The Bencliff Grit (10 to 14 ft) consists of yellowish false-bedded sands with large doggers (concretionary masses of calcareous sandstone). Osmington Oolite (60 ft) includes a mixed series of beds—white oolitic freestone, grey oolitic marl, nodular limestone and pisolite. Some beds are crowded with fossils (*Exogyra nana*, *Chlamys spp*. and other lamellibranchs).

The '*Trigonia*' *clavellata* Beds (14 ft) consisting of courses of reddish limestone are conspicuous by reason of the abundance of shells of *Myophorella* (*Vaugonia*) *clavellata*. Species of *Perisphinctes* occur and some beds are crowded with well-preserved lamellibranchs. Varying in thickness from 20 to 30 ft, the Sandsfoot Clay, grey, brown, or bluish in colour, is distinguished by the abundance of shells of the large triangular oyster *Liostrea delta*. Above is the Sandsfoot Grit, a reddish and greenish ferruginous sandstone with many fossils, among them the lamellibranch *Chlamys midas* and occasionally the ammonite *Ringsteadia*. At the type-locality (Sandsfoot Castle) the Sandsfoot Grit attains a thickness of 25 ft, but thins out eastwards. Above this grit is another clay-bed with seams of claystone. This is the Ringstead Waxy Clay, in which *Liostrea delta* appears in some abundance, and the ammonite *Ringsteadia anglica* also occurs. Marking the upper limit of the Corallian is the Ringstead Coral Bed, a greenish marly grit less than a foot in thickness and containing a large number of shells and corals. Among the fossils are the bivalved shells *Ctenostreon proboscideum* and *Camptonectes lens* and the corals *Thecosmilia annularis* and *Thamnasteria concinna*.

In a general way these subdivisions can be recognized in the inland outcrops, but variations in thickness and in lithic character are to be noted. The narrow outcrop of the formation can be traced between the vales of the Oxford and Kimmeridge Clays from Mappowder north of the Chalk downland to the northern limit of the Vale of Wardour, where it is faulted against the Upper Cretaceous beds that bound the Vale. North of Sturminster Newton the Osmington Oolite Beds yield building stones (the Marnhull and Todbere Freestones).

In the Vale of Pewsey the Corallian beds occupy a position similar to that in the Vale of Wardour; they extend from near Westbury in the south to Calne in the north. At Westbury, near the top of the series, is the Westbury Ironstone, a red and green oolitic rock 11 to 14 ft. thick; among the fossils in this bed are species of the ammonite *Ringsteadia*, *Liostrea delta* and other bivalves. At Steeple Ashton a coral reef (of the second cycle) has yielded abundant species of well-preserved corals, among them *Thecosmilia annularis* and *Comoseris irradians*. The Osmington Oolite at Calne has provided good building-stone—the Calne Freestone. Sea-urchins are common as fossils from this locality and are represented by several species, including the characteristic *Hemicidaris intermedia* and *Paracidaris florigemma*.

KIMMERIDGE CLAY

At the end of Corallian times changes in geographical conditions resulted in a gradual subsidence of the area and a long-continued deposition of muddy sediments. The clay formation known as the Kimmeridge Clay (on account of its full development in Kimmeridge Bay, Dorset) was thus laid down. The full thickness of this formation has only recently been determined, since a boring for oil in the type-area showed a depth of 581 ft below the last cliff-measurement by Arkell, making a total of 1,651 feet. Westwards, in the Ringstead area, it is not much more than 800 feet.

Certain variations in lithology are observable in the Kimmeridge Clay beds. In addition to thick clays there are thin bands of mudstone and several prominent stone-bands, some of which on account of their superior hardness form dangerous ledges on the coast (Pl. III A, and Fig. 9). In the upper part of the Kimmeridge Clay is a prominent band of calcareous mudstones with numerous ammonites of the species *Pavlovia rotunda*, which gives the name *rotunda* Nodules. The upper beds of the Kimmeridge Clay are best exposed in Hounstout Cliff, near St. Alban's Head. The succession here has been described by Arkell, who determined the following subdivisions. Above the *rotunda* Nodules, in upward order of succession, are the *Lingula* Shales (35 to 40 ft) named after the small brachiopod *Lingula*,

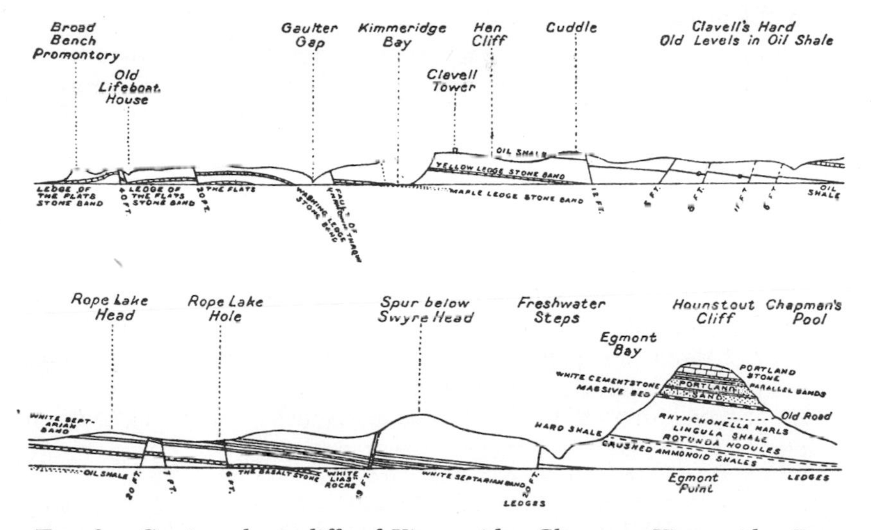

FIG. 9.—*Section along cliffs of Kimmeridge Clay near Kimmeridge Bay, Dorset*

(Adapted from W. J. Arkell, 'The Jurassic System in Great Britain,' 1933, p. 444) the *Rhynchonella* Marls (about 20 ft), with numerous examples of the brachiopod *Rhynchonella*, the Hounstout Clay (about 30 ft), apparently unfossiliferous, and the Hounstout Marl (40 to 50 ft), with thin layers of sandy cement-stone. Above is the Massive Bed, to be referred to later.

One of the most interesting beds in the Kimmeridge Clay formation is a bituminous shale which readily burns, producing a most unpleasant smell. The shale occurs as a layer less than 3 ft in thickness, and has long been known as 'Kimmeridge Coal.' This layer can be traced in the cliff-sections near Kimmeridge as also at Ringstead Bay. At the latter locality spontaneous ignition of the shale gave rise in 1826 to a fire that lasted for four years, and caused the place to be known as the Burning Cliff. The outcrop of the shale has also been traced in the neighbourhood of Portisham. Tests have been made from time to time with a view to its exploitation as a source of oil, but hitherto the high percentage of sulphur is one factor among others that has prevented its being used. Circular pieces of bituminous shale found in the soil near Kimmeridge have long been known as 'coal-money.' These pieces are probably the useless discs of larger pieces which had been turned on the lathe into ornamental objects. One side of the disc is flat, with three or four holes; the other is covered with mouldings.

The Kimmeridge Clay is well exposed on the Dorset coast between Gad Cliff and St. Alban's Head; it comes to the surface again, through faulting, in Ringstead Bay, and again near Osmington Mills, whence it extends inland westwards to Abbotsbury as a narrow tract of flat land between the rising edges of the Corallian beds on the south and the Portland beds on the north. Near the base of the formation at Abbotsbury is a remarkable bed of iron ore which in one place attains a thickness of 45 feet. The main bed is a reddish-brown oolitic rock full of shining pellets of ore in a matrix of fine quartz sand. The high percentage of silica militates against the ore being worked commercially to any great extent.

North of Abbotsbury the Jurassic strata are covered by the overstepping Upper Greensand, with the Chalk above, and the Kimmeridge Clay reappears north of the Dorset Heights where the Chalk outcrop swings northwards. Here it forms a fairly broad tract east of the ridge of Corallian beds until it enters the Vale of Wardour, where its further extension is cut out by overstepping Cretaceous strata and by faulting. Northwards it is covered for a distance of 11 miles, but crops out again in a broad expanse of the clay-land at the western end of the Vale of Pewsey.

Fossils are common throughout the Kimmeridge Clay, and include remains of saurians, crocodiles and fishes, as well as the commoner ammonites, lamellibranchs and brachiopods. As is the case with the other thick clay formations, zonal subdivision is possible by means of the species of ammonites. Other groups of fossils also have distinctive ranges although not

---

FIG. 10.—*Fossils from the Corallian and the Kimmeridge Clay.*

1. *Lingula ovalis* J. Sowerby; 2. Typical fragment of *Pavlovia rotunda* (J. Sowerby); 3. *Saccocoma sp.*, a pyritized radial plate from the Oil Shales (×4); 4. *Discinisca latissima* (J. Sowerby); 5, a, b. Left and right valves of *Exogyra nana* (J. Sowerby); 6, a, b. Left and right valves of *Chlamys* (*Radulopecten*) *fibrosa* (J. Sowerby); 7. *Rhactorhynchia inconstans* (J. Sowerby); 8. *Liostrea delta* (William Smith) (×½); 9. *Lucina miniscula* Blake; 10. *Exogyra virgula* Defrance; 11. *Thamnasteria concinna* (Goldfuss); 12. *Myophorella* (*Vaugonia*) *clavellata* (J. Sowerby); 13. *Thecosmilia annularis* (Fleming).

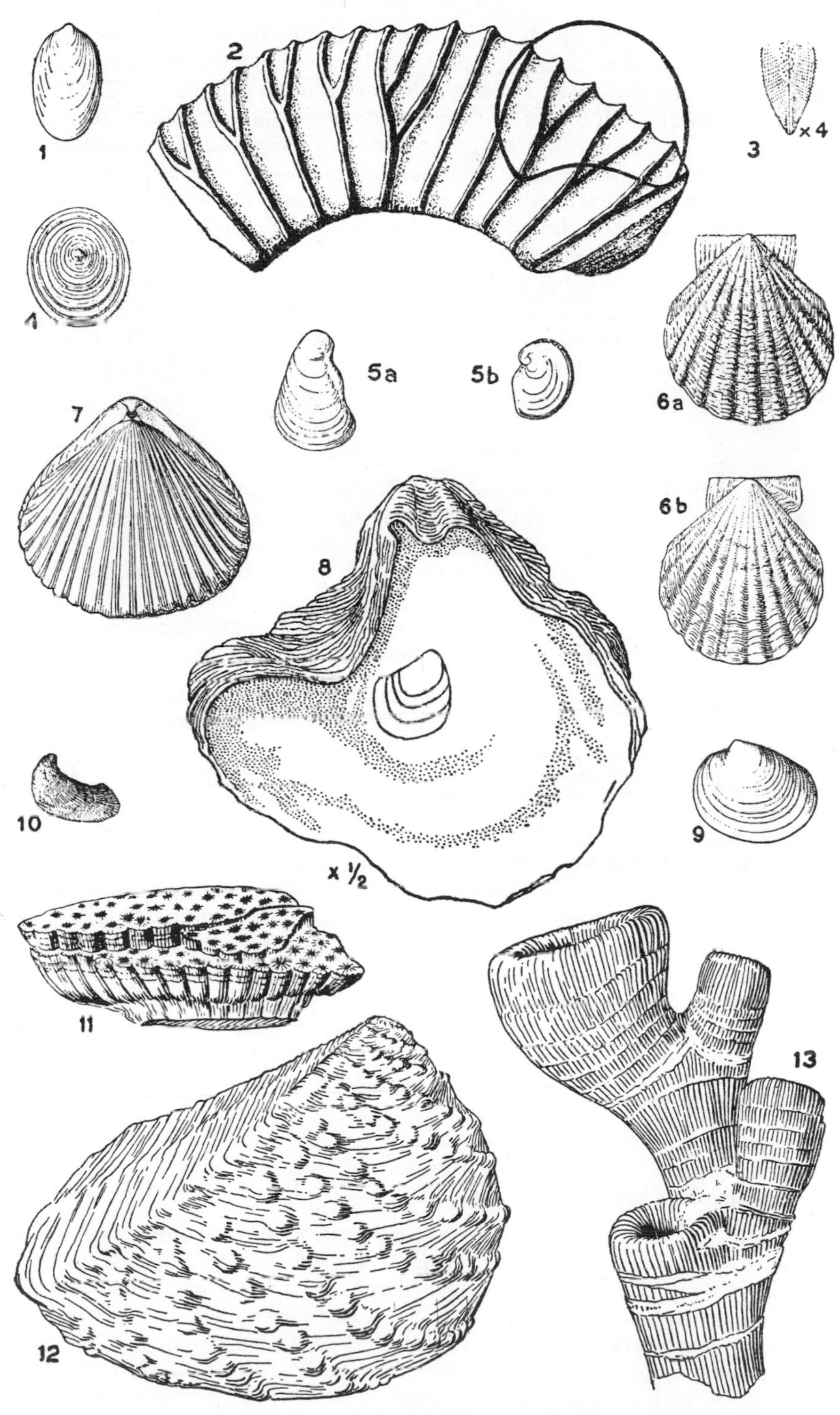

FIG. 10.—*Fossils from the Corallian and the Kimmeridge Clay*

so restricted as the ammonites. Thus the brachiopod *Rhactorhynchia inconstans* is typical of the lowest beds, while slightly higher in the succession shells of the large flat oyster *Liostrea delta* are found in abundance. The small, incurved, radially-ridged oyster *Exogyra virgula* is characteristic of the lower part of the formation, as also are the lamellibranchs *Lucina minuscula* and species of *Protocardia*. Among the brachiopods *Lingula ovalis* and *Discinisca latissima* have a long range but are more common in the upper part. A distinctive set of fossils is found in the Abbotsbury ironstone. These include ammonites (which prove the beds to be of Kimmeridge age, and not Corallian as was formerly thought) and brachiopods. Among the ammonites are species of *Rasenia*; and *Ornithella lampas* and *Rhactorhynchia pinguis* are typical brachiopods. The horizon of the oil-shale is indicated by the occurrence of small, isolated plates of the crinoid *Saccocoma*, always preserved in pyrites.

PORTLAND BEDS

A marked shallowing of the sea took place at the end of Kimmeridge Clay times, and the succeeding sediments show a gradual passage from the clay to a series of sands, sandstones and marly beds, yellowish brown and greenish-grey or blue in colour, and darker at the base. Thick bands of sandstones and lines of sandy cement-stone are conspicuous in these beds. This series, known as the Portland Sands, attains a maximum thickness of 120 ft; above are the Portland Stone beds.

For some time the line of division between the Kimmeridge Clay and the Portland Sands was a matter of varying opinion. Fitton, who proposed the name Portland Sands in 1827, evidently intended the boundary to be at the top of what is now known as the Hounstout Clay, referred to on p. 26, for he mentions the springs that break out at the base of the sands. But the boundary selected by the Survey in 1898, and adopted by later workers, is a conspicuous stone band (5 ft thick) on Hounstout Cliff (Fig. 9). This bed, known as the Massive Bed, consists of hard calcareous sandstone which weathers brown or yellow, and is to be seen about 50 ft above the old road round the cliff. The Massive Bed is characterized by numerous specimens of a small oyster, a variety of *Exogyra nana*, the brachiopod '*Rhynchonella*' *portlandica* and ammonites with sheaf-like ribbing, *Zaraiskites albani*. In the upper part of the Portland Sands a much larger ammonite, *Glaucolithites gorei* is found. The gradual change from the Kimmeridge Clay to the Portland Stone is reflected in the contour of the ground; the profile of the northern end of the Isle of Portland and that of certain of the cliffs in the south of Purbeck show the gentle inclination of the Kimmeridge Clay passing into the intermediate slope of the Portland Sands, which leads to the steep wall of the Portland Stone Series.

To the presence of the Portland Stone Series are due some of the most prominent features of the Dorset coast. On the Isle of Purbeck between Durlston Head and St. Alban's Head they form almost perpendicular walls rising to a height of 200 feet. From St. Alban's Head they run inland and form projecting spurs above the low ground of the Kimmeridge Clay, and, extending westwards, come to the coast again in Gad Cliff. Here the beds are inclined to the north, and they become more tilted farther west as they

A. BROAD BENCH AND CLIFFS, WEST OF KIMMERIDGE BAY, DORSET

B. CLIFFS OF LOWER GREENSAND (CRACKERS GROUP), SOUTH-EAST OF ATHERFIELD POINT, ISLE OF WIGHT

(*For details see p.* iv)

A. CLIFFS OF PURBECK AND PORTLAND BEDS AT BLACK NOR, PORTLAND

B. SUCKTHUMB QUARRY, PORTLAND
(*For details see p.* iv)

get closer to the Purbeck Fold. They continue as the Mupe Rocks and extend westwards as a margin to the coast, broken away at the entrance to Lulworth Cove and breached in two places at the bottom of Stair Hole, beyond which they may be traced as the Man o' War Rocks and again in the rampart of Durdle Door.

Nearly the whole of the Isle of Portland is formed of Portland Beds, with a covering of Purbeck Beds, of which a considerable part has been removed by quarrying (Fig. 11). Its shores are strewn with blocks of stone either thrown over in quarrying or broken away by landslips, as on the eastern side (Pl. V A). The Island is the remnant of the southern limb of the Weymouth anticline, as is shown by the gentle southward dip of the beds, the underlying Kimmeridge Clay coming to the surface only at the northern end. On the northern limb of the Weymouth anticline the outcrop of the Portland Beds extends with few interruptions from the faulted mass below Holworth House, in Ringstead Bay, to near Portisham. Near Poxwell the beds are arranged in the form of an inverted boat, or elongated dome with sharp north and south dips, a structure known as a pericline. This pericline brings up an inlier of Portland Sands, which forms undulating meadows bordered by scarps of Portland Stone, the resulting features being a picturesque hollow more than a mile in length, known as the Poxwell Circus.

To the north of the area affected by the Weymouth anticline the Portland Beds are concealed by the Chalk uplands. The formation is exposed again, however, in the Vale of Wardour and the Vale of Pewsey, two areas on the western margin of the Chalk where erosion has followed upheaval.

Portland Stone Series.—In general terms the Portland Stone Series of Dorset consists of a Cherty Series below and a Freestone Series above. Considerable variation, however, is to be observed in the different beds of this series, not only in lithic character but also in thickness (Fig. 13). This variation is an important feature since the Portland Stone Series provides the building stone for which this district has long been famous (Fig. 14). The following is the general succession on the Isle of Portland, but the beds vary even within this limited area, and differ considerably from those on the mainland.

(At the top)

THE ROACH (average thickness 3 ft): a greyish oolitic limestone, honeycombed with hollow moulds and casts of shells.

WHIT BED (7–15 ft): a buff-coloured oolitic limestone with tiny shell-fragments. The best freestone.

FLINTY BED (2 ft): chert.

CURF (0–4 ft): soft chalky limestone.

LITTLE ROACH (0–3 ft): similar to the main roach bed but impersistent.

BASE BED (5–10 ft): soft pale-buff oolitic limestone of fine texture. A good freestone.

CHERT BEDS (60–70 ft): chalky limestone with layers of chert nodules similar to flint. At the bottom is a BASAL SHELL BED (7–8 ft), a hard limestone crowded with small shells and small worm-tubes.

In this succession it will be noted that the Base Bed is at the bottom of the building-stone beds and the Whit Bed at the top; but on account of the variation in the beds the terms are applicable to types of stone rather than actual horizons.

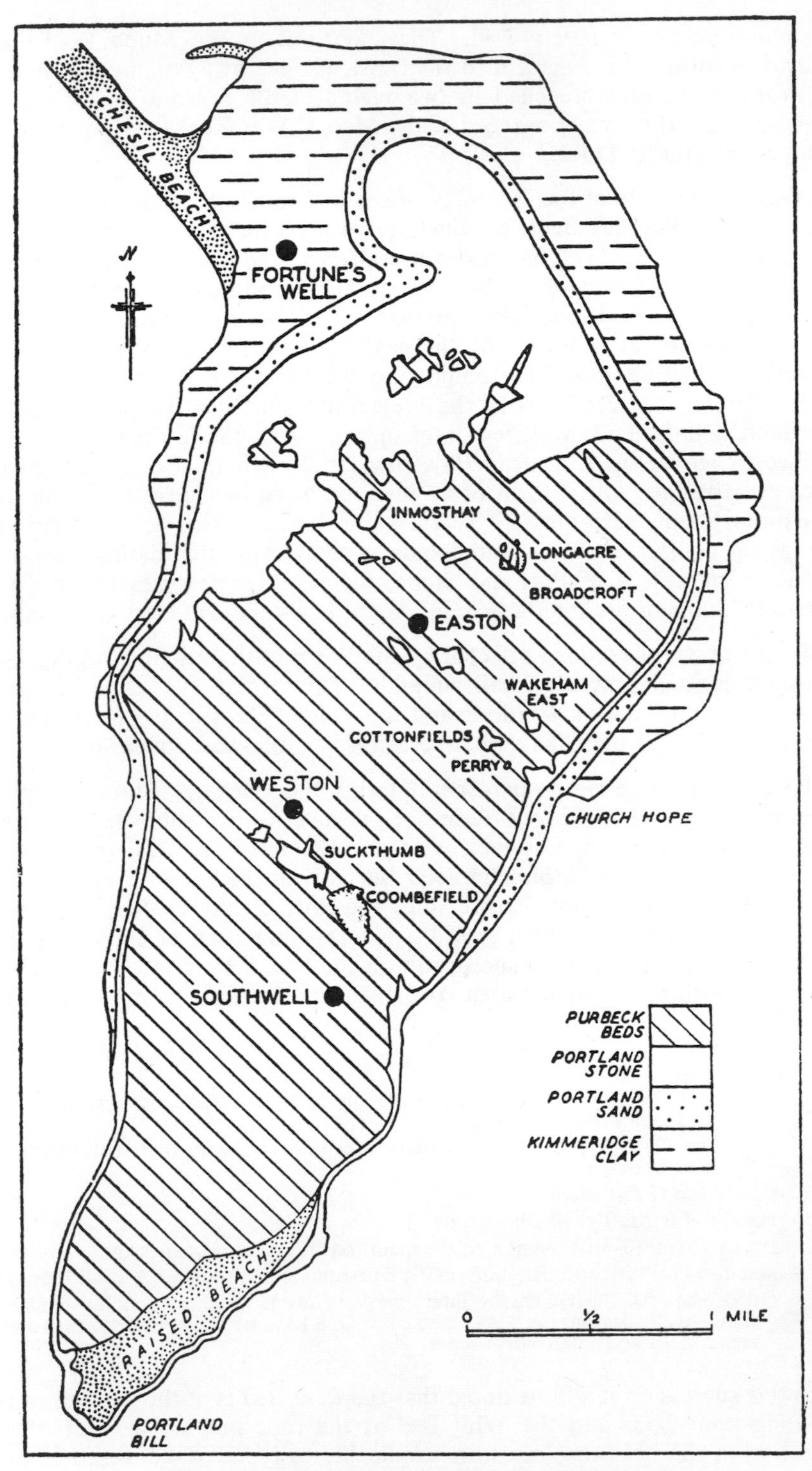

FIG. 11.—*Sketch-map of the Isle of Portland*

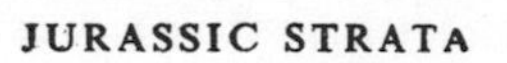

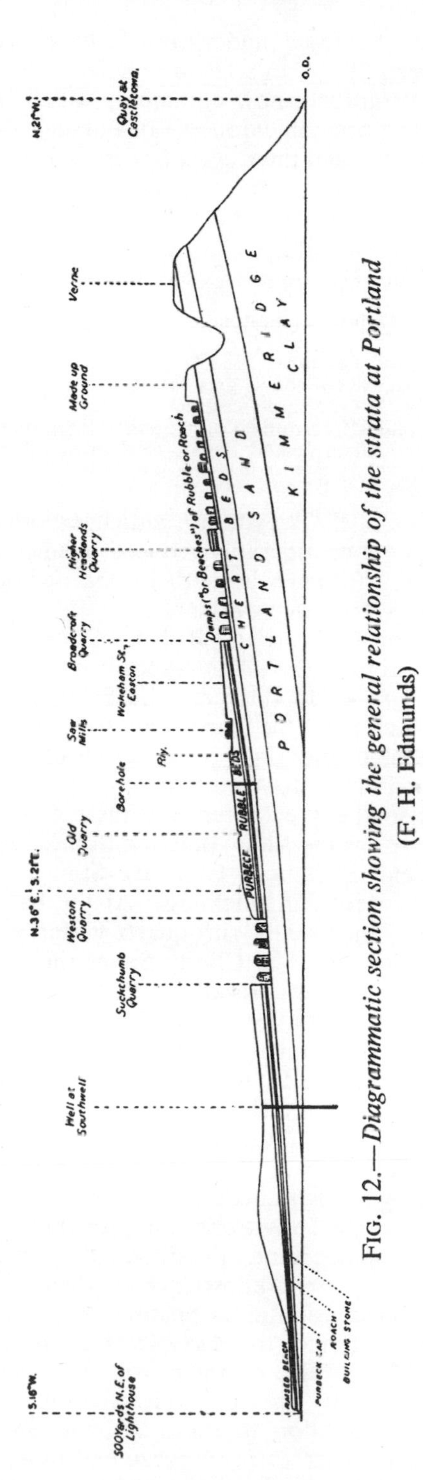

FIG. 12.—*Diagrammatic section showing the general relationship of the strata at Portland*
(F. H. Edmunds)

A number of quarries, some underground, have been worked in the Isle of Purbeck between St. Alban's Head and Durlston Head, but several, particularly those underground, now commonly called caves, *e.g.* the Tilly Whim Caves, have long been abandoned. In Purbeck the Freestone Series attains a thickness of 50 ft, and the Cherty Series 70 feet. Here the following succession is recognized:—

(At the top)
SHRIMP BED (8–16 ft): fine-grained white limestone.
BLUE BED or SPANGLE (10 ft): grey, shelly limestone with the large ammonite *Titanites*.
POND FREESTONE (7 ft): oolitic limestone.
CHERT VEIN (2–4 ft).
LISTY BED (6–9 in): soft freestone.
HOUSE CAP or SPANGLE (8 ft): coarse grey limestone.
UNDER PICKING CAP (2–3 ft): hard freestone.
UNDER FREESTONE (8–11 ft): cream-coloured oolitic limestone.
CHERTY SERIES (the Cliff or Inland Beds): hard brown limestone with veins and nodules of chert.

On the northern side of the Weymouth anticline both the Freestone Beds and the Cherty Series are considerably reduced in thickness; at Upwey the building stone is only 3 ft, while both there and at Portisham the Cherty Series is conspicuous in its chalky whiteness.

In the Vale of Wardour the Portland Beds have been quarried for building stone for several centuries, the chief exposures being around Tisbury, Chilmark and Chicksgrove. In this area the Portland Sand is about 60 ft in thickness. The lower part (the Basement Beds, 30 to 40 ft) comprises brown and greenish sand and clays with hardened patches of sand and thin stone beds. A bed of gritstone containing pebbles of lydite (interesting as marking the most southerly occurrence of these pebbles) has been found in this division. Above are the Main Building Stones, which attain a thickness of 18 ft, and yield the famous Chilmark Stone. The Portland Stone Series is not more than 50 ft in thickness. At the base are the Ragstone Beds (8 to 10 ft), shelly limestones with quartz grains, comparable with the Basal Shell Bed of Portland. The Cherty Series (here the Chalky Series), soft limestones with black chert, recall the beds of Upwey and Portisham in their chalky whiteness. Locally, near Tisbury, a vein of chert, long ago quarried away, yielded abundant remains of corals so well preserved in the hard silica that they were called 'starred agates.' Corresponding with the Freestone Series of Portland are the Upper Building Stones of the Vale of Wardour. These are siliceous limestones, white or buff-coloured and fine-grained, passing locally into 'roach.'

In the Vale of Pewsey Portland beds crop out near Potterne, Coulston and Crockwood. The three chief divisions are probably represented, but the present exposures are unimportant. Fossils are to be found throughout the Portland Beds, but our present knowledge of their distribution does not permit such detailed subdivision as is possible in some other Jurassic formations. Ammonites referred to *Zaraiskites albani* have already been mentioned from the Massive Bed on the coast; other examples of this genus have also been found slightly higher in this division. In the upper part of the Portland Sands, in addition to the ammonite *Glaucolithites* are beds crowded with the small oyster *Exogyra nana*, and other lamellibranchs and brachiopods are common. For the divisions above this it can be stated in

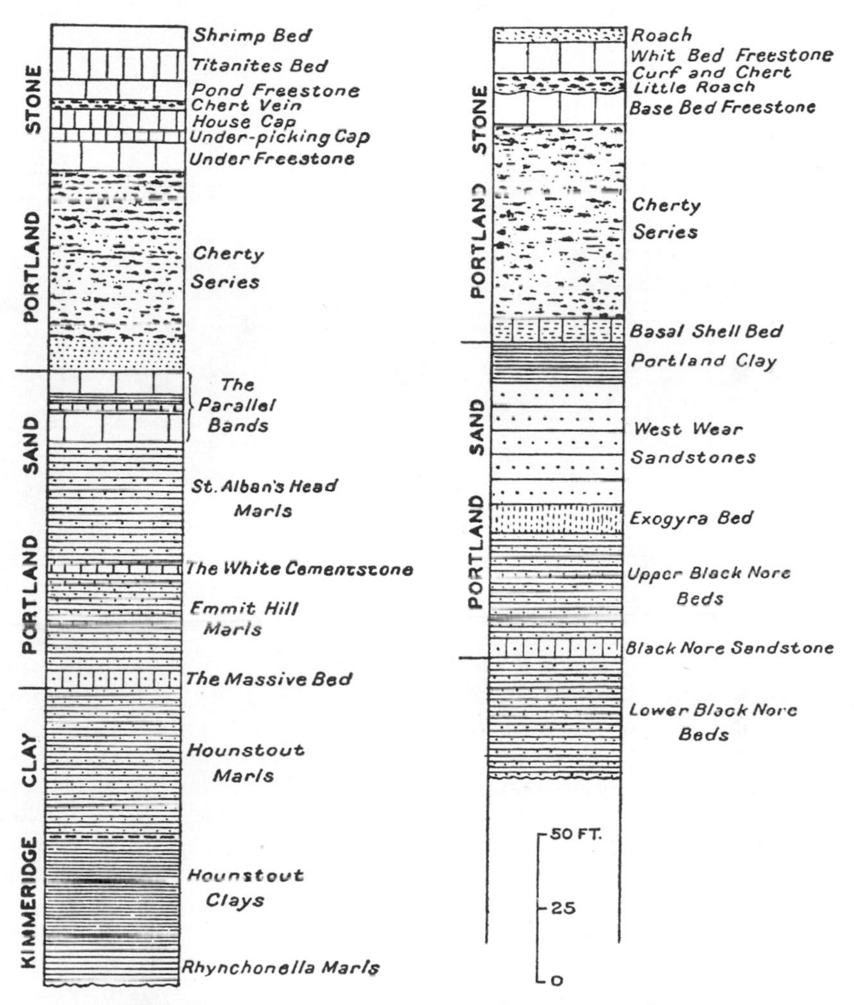

FIG. 13.—*Comparative sections of the Portland Beds and subjacent strata* (After W. J. Arkell, ' The Jurassic System in Great Britain,' 1933, p. 495)

general terms that the Cherty Series yield ammonites of the genus *Kerberites*, while the giant ammonites, *Titanites*, familiar objects in Portland, come from the Freestone Series. Bivalved shells are the most common fossils and are the most widely distributed. The most frequent species are *Protocardia dissimilis*, *Camptonectes* (*Camptochlamys*) *lamellosus*, *Isognomon listeri* (formerly known as *Perna bouchardi*), *Pleuromya tellina* and *Laevitrigonia gibbosa*. The last-named species (known locally as 'horses' heads') and the gastropod *Aptyxiella portlandica*, the ' Portland Screw ', are the commonest fossils represented as casts and moulds in the Roach. In places the annelid *Serpula gordialis* forms a rock-bed (serpulite) in the Cherty Series; it is also abundant in the upper part of the Portland Sands. Remains of marine reptiles, chelonians and fishes are found occasionally in the Portland rocks.

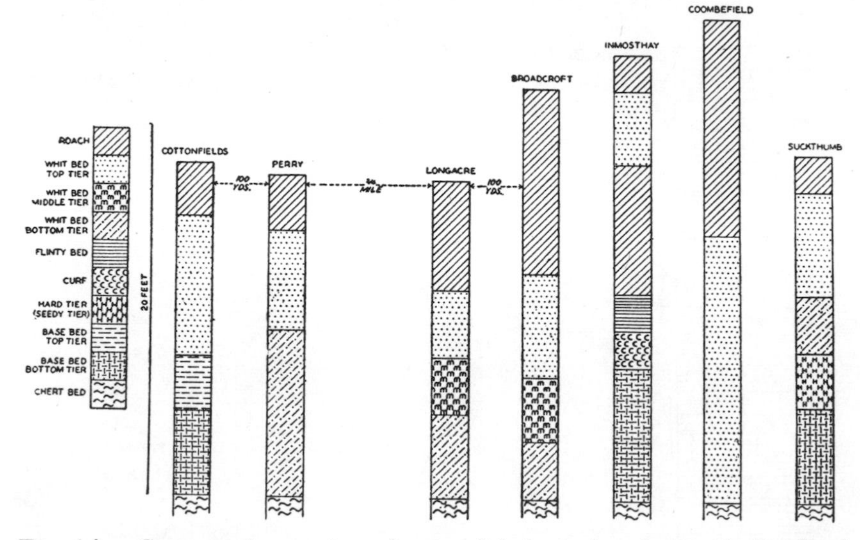

FIG. 14.—*Comparative sections showing lithological variations in Portland limestone at quarries shown on map, Fig.* 11
(After F. H. Edmunds, *Proc. Geol. Assoc.*, vol. xliii, 1932, p. 231)

PURBECK BEDS

Once again the relative distribution of land and sea underwent considerable modification. The shallow sea, under which the Portland Beds were formed, retreated and its place was taken by an oscillating area, sometimes a land-surface, sometimes covered by swamps and freshwater lakes or brackish waters, or occupied by mud flats. From time to time the sea invaded this unstable area. As a result of these changes a varied series of deposits was accumulated, and since they are particularly well developed in the Isle of Purbeck they are known as the Purbeck Beds. The remains of life preserved in the various beds bear testimony to the altered conditions. 'Dirt-beds,' or fossil soils, containing trunks of trees often with stumps and roots still in position, mark former land-surfaces. Layers of gypsum and pseudomorphs of rock-salt indicate the former presence of land-locked lagoons, subject at times to be dried slowly. Insects of many orders abounded nearby, and their remains drifted or were blown into the waters, while Iguanodon-like dinosaurs and a variety of small mammals browsed on the land, and dwarf crocodiles inhabited the marshes. Occasional invasions of the sea left behind deposits containing marine shells such as *Trigonia* and *Isognomon*; and the most widespread marine episode is marked by a thick oyster-bank of wide extent.

In Durlston Bay, where a full succession can be seen, the Purbeck Beds attain a thickness of nearly 400 ft (Fig. 15). They become thinner westwards (290 ft at Worbarrow), decreasing rapidly near Lulworth, but become thicker again (189 ft) at Ridgeway. Many different beds are recognizable, and divisions of Lower, Middle and Upper have been estabished, but on account of varying lithology they cannot readily be arranged into obvious groups, nor do the larger fossils assist in this respect. Most of the beds, however, contain the remains of tiny crustaceans called ostracods, and a study of the distribution of species shows that the occurrence of these small fossils corresponds with the threefold division, although there is an overlapping of species in the Middle Purbeck. The distribution of ostracods in geological time, as marked by their occurrence at different horizons in the strata, is sufficiently restricted to enable Purbeck beds in different places to be correlated.

The following is the general succession in the Isle of Purbeck.

Lower Purbeck.—Where the lowest bed of the Purbeck series can be seen in contact with the uppermost bed of the Portland series, as at Pondfield (Worbarrow) and at Lulworth, the junction is clear and sharp and the two beds stratigraphically parallel and conformable. The marine Portland beds were therefore raised above sea-level without folding or fracture. The first of the Purbeck beds to be deposited were the Caps and the Dirt-beds, the thickness of this division varying from 9 to 19 feet. The Caps consist of two bands of tufaceous limestone, a Hard Cap below and a Soft Cap above. At the base of these Caps, as a rule, are the Dirt-beds. A good view of the Lower Purbeck Beds is to be seen at the Fossil Forest, on the sloping ledge at the top of the cliffs east of Lulworth Cove (Pl. VI B). Here the highly inclined Portland Stone is overlain directly by Hard Cap, on which is a Dirt-bed (6-18 in.), composed of black earth and a goodly proportion of limestone pebbles. The trees which grew on the soil which is now the Dirt-bed were subsequently silicified, and their stumps and prostrate trunks can be seen enveloped by the Soft Cap, composed of carbonate of lime deposited around them probably by the action of freshwater algae in the shallow waters that then covered the area.

Above the Cap Beds of the Fossil Forest is a remarkable development known as the Broken Beds, which here attain a maximum thickness of 15 feet. The interesting feature of these beds is that although they present a shattered or brecciated appearance, the broken bands of limestone being in separate pieces and set at all angles, the overlying beds are quite undisturbed. One explanation, put forward by Osmond Fisher over a century ago, was that this phenomenon was due to the collapse of the beds during Purbeck times through the decay of the vegetation on which they were deposited; and this was generally accepted for many years. Arkell included the Broken Beds in his study of the problems of the tectonics of the Lulworth area and has shown that the collapse hypothesis is unacceptable. Evidently more than one process was involved, and it is likely that a plane of weakness was first originated, through the hydration of anhydrite to form gypsum, which was afterwards removed by solution, as suggested by Professor S. E. Hollingworth. The beds subsequently became involved in the movements that produced the Purbeck Fold in Tertiary times, and their present jumbled arrangement is the result of adjustment between the strong Portland Stone and the weakened Purbeck beds.

The Caps and Broken Beds form only the lowest part of the Lower Purbeck; the greater part of this division consists of marls and clays, which reach a

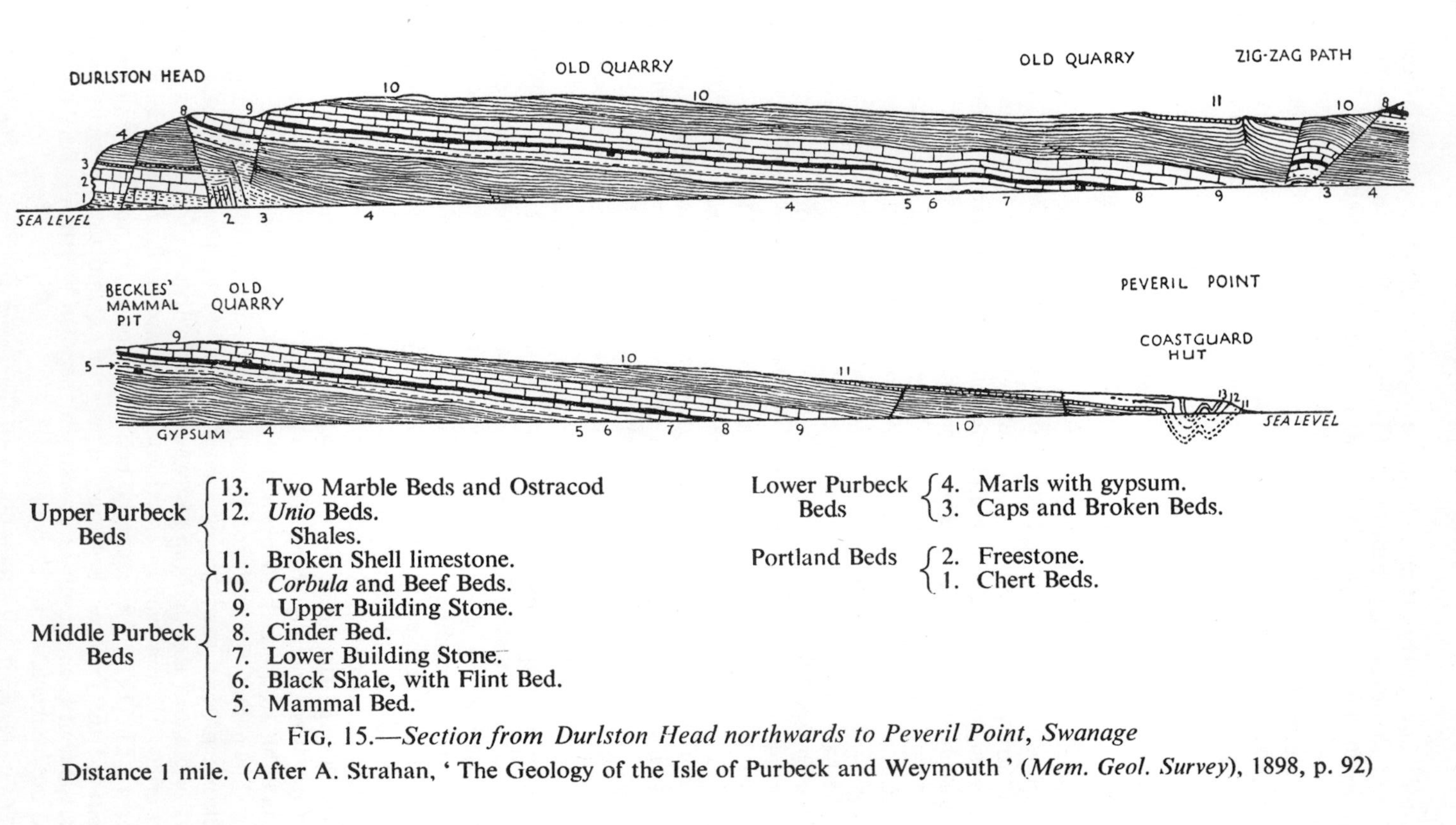

FIG. 15.—*Section from Durlston Head northwards to Peveril Point, Swanage*

Distance 1 mile. (After A. Strahan, 'The Geology of the Isle of Purbeck and Weymouth' (*Mem. Geol. Survey*), 1898, p. 92) thickness of as much as 135 feet. The conditions of deposition of these beds were very variable, for the strata differ in lithic character, as also in the nature of the fossils found in them. Shales and freestones abound in remains of ostracods; some mudstones have surfaces almost covered with the isopod *Archaeoniscus*; certain black cherts include remains of the siliceous sponge *Spongilla*; while incursions of the sea left behind beds with the marine shell *Protocardia purbeckensis* in such abundance that the beds have been called Cockle Beds. Muddy salt-water lakes were also formed, and evaporation gave rise to beds of gypsum and crystals of rock-salt, now preserved as casts. Remains of shells are very uncommon near the beds with gypsum, but insect-remains were washed into or blown into the brine in large numbers, with the result that ' insect-beds ' were formed.

Middle Purbeck.—A further change in geographical conditions took place at the end of Lower Purbeck times, for in Durlston Bay the base of the Middle Purbeck is marked by a Dirt-bed (1 ft) known as the Mammal Bed. This bed is of considerable interest on account of the remains of remarkable mammals found in it; it yields also bones of crocodiles, including unique dwarfed forms. The beds which follow are called the Lower Building Stone beds because of the presence, in the upper part, of workable beds of cream-coloured stone. These beds, which attain a maximum thickness of 34 ft, are largely of freshwater origin. They include a conspicuous bed of white limestone (3 ft) with nodules of black chert. The lower part consists mostly of shales and marls, laid down in waters wherein ostracods were abundant. Investigations by Dr. F. W. Anderson have thrown interesting light on the relationship between the salt-content of the shales and the distribution of the species of ostracods. Evidently the waters tended to become increasingly saline, but the salinity was lowered periodically by influxes of fresh water.

Above the Lower Building Stones is a bed which indicates the most considerable change in conditions in Purbeck times, namely, an invasion of the sea which spread over a large part of the south of England. This marine episode left behind it a conspicuous bed made up almost entirely of oyster-shells. From its appearance when seen in a weathered condition this bed is known as the Cinder Bed, and it is present in the Vale of Wardour as well as in South Dorset. In addition to the oysters (*Liostrea distorta*) it includes occasional shells such as ' *Trigonia*,' *Isognomon* [*Perna*] and *Protocardia*, while the occurrence of *Hemicidaris purbeckensis*, a small sea-urchin, is of especial interest. The Cinder Bed separates the Lower Building Stones from an upper series varying in thickness up to 50 ft; and the stone beds of both series have been mined extensively in Purbeck between Kingston and Durlston. Several beds in the Upper Building Stones contain marine shells (*Gervillia obtusa*, *Corbula*, *Pecten*, etc.) but they alternate with beds of freshwater or estuarine origin, as indicated by the presence of such shells as *Valvata helicoides* and *Hydrobia chopardiana*. This upper series has also yielded interesting remains of reptiles and fishes.

The Upper Building Stones are succeeded by layers of shelly limestone, shales and marls, with ' beef ' and selenite. That these beds are of marine origin is shown by the profusion of the small bivalved shell *Corbula*, together with *Protocardia*, *Modiolus*, *Ostrea*, etc. The beds yield also remains of turtle, fishes, ostracods and insects; they are known as the *Corbula* Beds, and attain a thickness of 34 feet. At the top of the Middle Purbeck series are the Chief Beef Beds (8 to 30 ft), consisting of layers of limestone and shales-with-beef and selenite. The bivalved shell *Neomiodon* (formerly known as *Cyrena*) occurs, in abundance, chiefly in a crushed condition.

Upper Purbeck.—Freshwater conditions prevailed almost without interruption towards the close of Purbeck times, for the Upper Purbeck beds all show evidence of having been so deposited. At the base is the Broken Shell Limestone or Burr, composed to a large extent of shell fragments, and attaining a thickness of 10 feet. Above are clays with layers of beef and bands of greenish limestone with shells of the freshwater mussel *Unio*. These are the *Unio* Beds (5 to 6 ft in thickness). The higher part of the Upper Purbeck is important as yielding the famous Purbeck Marble. This material occurs in two layers, red and green, and has been used for interior decoration in churches; it is made up to a large extent of the univalve shell *Viviparus* (formerly known as *Paludina*). The Marble Beds include layers of marl, clay, thin bands of limestone with innumerable ostracods and shales-with-beef. At the top of the Upper series are the *Viviparus* Clays (1 to 11 ft) not seen at Swanage, which consist of coloured clays and marls of variable thickness, and contain abundant shells of *Viviparus*. These clays are exposed at Worbarrow Bay and Mupe Bay.

On the Isle of Portland the Lower Purbeck beds alone are present. These correspond only in general character with the development in Purbeck; the thickness is variable, being 100 ft at the most, and in places considerably less. The Dirt-beds, the tree-trunks and the tufaceous Caps bear comparison with similar features on the mainland. Above are beds that have local names: aish, a soft, earthy limestone, often stained red; the slats, or layers of fissile limestone.

In the Jurassic area north of Weymouth the Purbeck beds have been quarried for building stone near Upwey. The formation crops out again in the Vale of Wardour, but is thinner; the tiny ostracods show, however, that all three divisions are represented. The beds are quarried at several places between Dinton and Tisbury.

FIG. 16.—*Fossils from the Portland and the Purbeck Beds.*

1. *Cypridea propunctata* Sylvester-Bradley (× 30); 2. *Cypridea fasciculata* (Forbes) (× 30); 3. ‘ *Cypris* ’ *purbeckensis* Forbes (× 30); 4. *Corbula alata* J. de C. Sowerby; 5. *Protocardia purbeckensis* (de Loriol); 6. *Liostrea distorta* (J. de. C. Sowerby); 7. *Archaeoniscus brodiei* Milne Edwards; 8. *Physa bristovii* Phillips; 9. *Viviparus inflatus* (Sandberger) 10. *Pachycheilus manselli* (de Loriol); 11. *Neomiodon medius* (J. de. C. Sowerby); 12. *Protocardia dissimilis* (J. de C. Sowerby) (× ⅔); 13. *Camptonectes* (*Camptochlamys*) *lamellosus* (J. Sowerby) (× ½); 14, 15. *Aptyxiella portlandica* (J. de C. Sowerby) (15, natural cast); 16. *Pleuromya tellina* (Agassiz); 17. *Mytilus* (*Falcimytilus*) *suprajurensis* Cox; 18. *Myophorella incurva* (Benett) (natural cast).

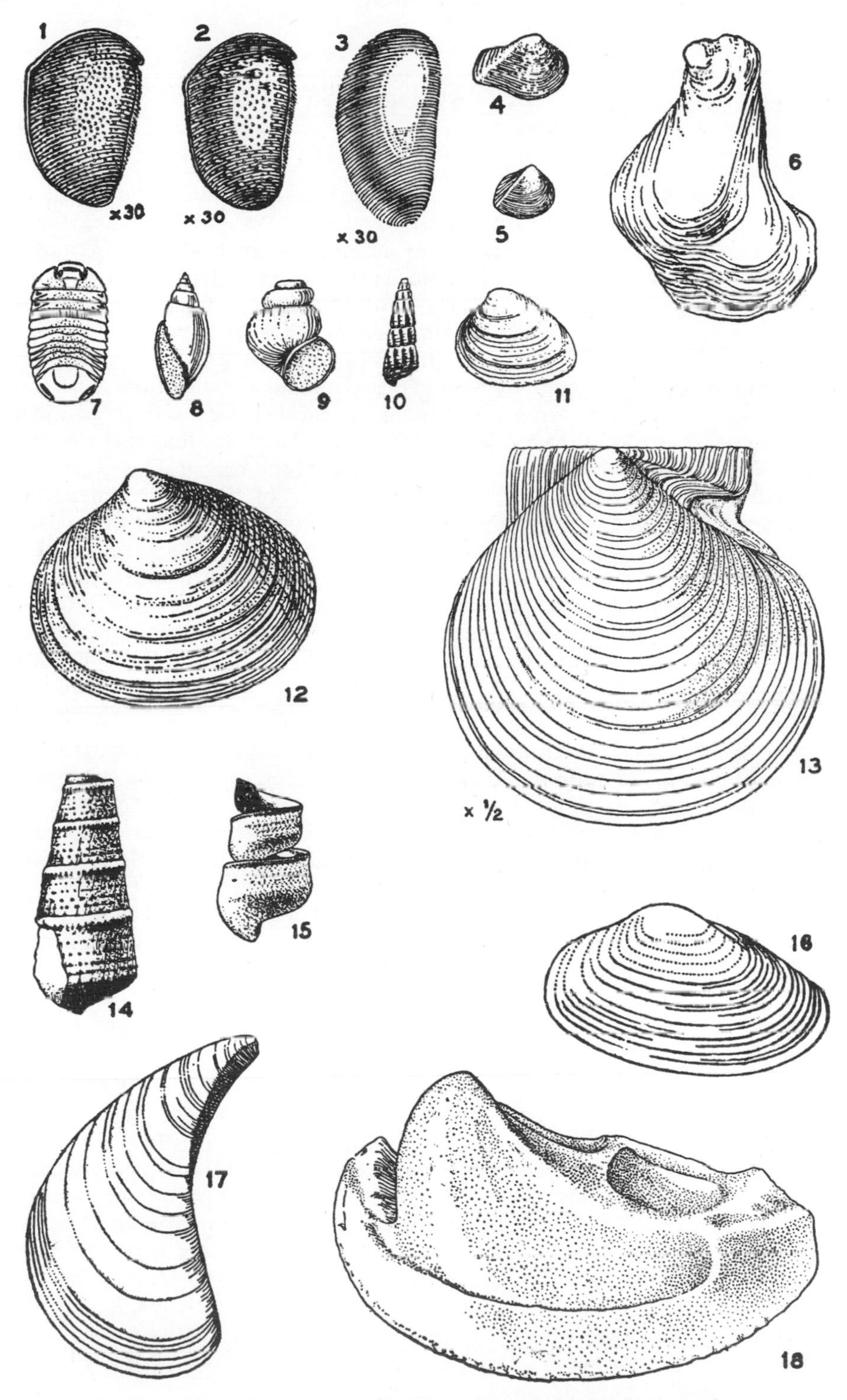

FIG. 16.—*Fossils from the Portland and the Purbeck Beds*

III. CRETACEOUS STRATA

WEALDEN

BOTH IN THE Vale of Wardour and in south Dorset the uppermost beds of the Purbeck pass upwards gradually into sandy clays and laminated sands and clays which actually belong to another formation—the Wealden. In this part of the country there is no definite line of division between the two formations, whether we look for it in the nature of the strata or in the evidence of the fossils. Yet the separation of the two is important from the point of view of classification, for the Wealden beds are here the earliest deposits of the Cretaceous System. To understand the significance of this uninterrupted passage from one system to another we need to consider deposits farther afield, particularly to the east. There we find that the new beds (the Wealden), which rest evenly on the Purbeck beds in Dorset, stretch across older strata which lay beyond the margin of the Purbeck deposits. Evidence for this was found through the deep borings in southern England and northern France. Meanwhile the Cretaceous age of the Wealden beds has been proved by comparison with similar strata in north-west Germany, where they pass laterally into marine beds and can thus be fitted into the scheme of classification. The history of the Lower Cretaceous Period in England has been studied by Dr. J. F. Kirkaldy, whose investigations have enabled him to present a clearer picture of the physical conditions than was formerly possible.

At the end of Jurassic times our area was evidently near sea-level and was covered largely by swamps and lagoons. The beginning of Cretaceous times was marked by an uplift of the surrounding higher land, and probably by a change in climate because it was accompanied by a revival of active rivers. These rivers, draining a land area in the west, spread their detritus over southern England and northern France in the form of extensive delta-flats, with large lagoons. The deposits are of varied character, including coloured sands, sandstones, grits, mottled clays and shales. Lignite occurs in abundance and occasional tree-trunks and rolled bones are found. In the Purbeck area the Wealden beds include an abundance of quartz pebbles and quartz grit, which was obviously brought from the west by river action; and the constituent material of the beds generally is coarser westwards. Beds in eastern Purbeck contain heavy minerals that were derived from the Dartmoor granite mass.

When sedimentation decreased through the lowering of the surrounding land masses, large freshwater lagoons were formed, and the deposits of these waters gave rise to finely-laminated shales. For the most part, sedimentation kept pace with subsidence, but occasional periods of emergence, when the deposits became dry enough for large reptiles to roam over them, are indicated by the presence of suncracks or footprints. One interesting feature, indicative of the origin of these beds, is the ‘ Pine Raft,’ visible at low tide near Brook Chine, in the Isle of Wight. This is a mass of prostrate tree-trunks that were evidently washed into the delta, where they became water-logged and stranded.

The Wealden beds thin out in the west, north and east. Their development in our area shows a thickness of 2,350 ft at Swanage; thence to the west they become coarser and conglomeratic, and decrease rapidly in thickness, being 1,200 ft in Worbarrow Bay, 750 ft at Mupe Bay, and 350 ft at Upwey, near Weymouth. Their further extension westwards was eroded during the deposition of a later marine formation. The beds are well exposed on the Dorset coast in the five great sections at Swanage, Worbarrow and Mupe Bays, at Lulworth Cove and Durdle Promontory. In the north of the area they are exposed in the Vale of Wardour with a much reduced thickness.

In the Isle of Wight, where the upper part of the Wealden Series is brought to the surface by two anticlines (*see* p. 89), two distinct divisions can be recognized. The lower division comprises the Wealden Marls or Variegated Clays; the upper is the Wealden Shales. The Marls are red, purple, green and variegated clays and marls, with bands of sandstone, sand and sandy limestones; they contain much driftwood, ferns, fruits of conifers and shells (among them the freshwater snail *Viviparus spp.* and the freshwater mussel *Unio valdensis*). Fish-remains and water-worn bones of large reptiles (*Iguanodon*) are also to be found. The Shales are dull blue or blackish clays with layers of clay-ironstone, sandstone and shelly limestone; their even bedding and dull hue present a marked contrast to the coloured and massive Marls. Some of the shale-layers are so finely bedded as to constitute ' paper-shales '; their surfaces are often crowded with the remains of ostracods. Near the base of the Shales in Brixton Bay is a red, sandy bed interesting on account of the remains of the small dinosaur *Hypsilophodon* that it contains. Higher up in the series, and conspicuous in the cliffs is a massive bed of sandstone, the sandstone of Barnes High (Fig. 17). Among the larger fossils of the Shales, in addition to the shells mentioned as occurring in the Marls, are the bivalve *Filosina gregaria* and sundry species of ferns. In the upper beds oyster-shells and the brackish-water univalve *Paraglauconia strombiformis* are common.

The Wealden Marls are of freshwater origin, but in the highest beds of the Shales there is evidence of the proximity of marine conditions. At the end of Wealden times earth-movements that had been in progress became more appreciable and eventually the sea, advancing from the south, broke over most of the area of the Wealden delta. It occupied the South of England as far west as the centre of Dorset and extended northwards through Wiltshire, laying down a series of deposits called the Lower Greensand. The line of junction between the two formations is sharply defined, and it is evident that some of the Wealden beds were eroded by the advancing sea because at the base of the Lower Greensand are fossils from the Wealden and even older beds. Thus began the Cretaceous Period of marine deposition, a period which was accompanied by considerable variation in sea-conditions and culminated in the laying down of the extensive Chalk formation.

LOWER GREENSAND

This division includes a variety of beds, not only sands but clay-beds, sandstone and grit; the name was applied because of the prevalent green

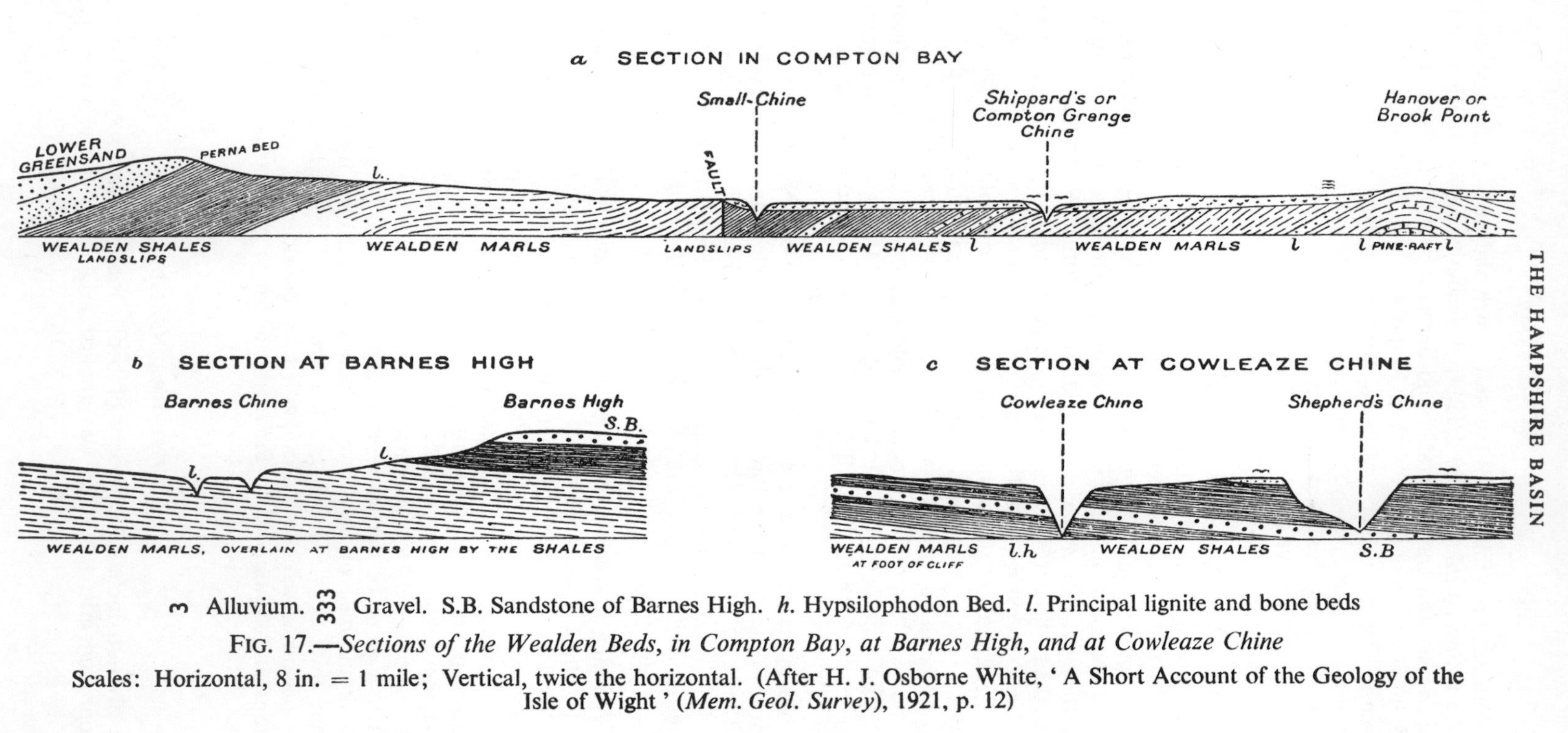

Alluvium. Gravel. S.B. Sandstone of Barnes High. *h.* Hypsilophodon Bed. *l.* Principal lignite and bone beds

FIG. 17.—*Sections of the Wealden Beds, in Compton Bay, at Barnes High, and at Cowleaze Chine*

Scales: Horizontal, 8 in. = 1 mile; Vertical, twice the horizontal. (After H. J. Osborne White, 'A Short Account of the Geology of the Isle of Wight' (*Mem. Geol. Survey*), 1921, p. 12)

tint of many of the sands. The freshness of the green coloration, however, soon wears off on exposure, and the usual appearance is that of a rusty brown. In the Isle of Wight and in places in the Isle of Purbeck the lowest bed (6 ft or less), generally a sandy clay passing up into a ferruginous grit, is characterized by a large, thick, strongly-ribbed shell *Mulletia* [*Perna*] *mulleti*, and is known as the *Perna* Bed.

The fullest development of the Lower Greensand in the area is in the south of the Isle of Wight, where (near Atherfield) it attains a thickness of 800 ft (Fig. 18). It decreases in thickness eastwards, westwards and northwards, being 600 ft in the eastern end of the Island, 400 ft in the west, while at Punfield, on the Dorset coast, it is less than 200 ft, it does not reach 50 ft in the Vale of Wardour. In Dorset the formation is not found farther west than Mupe Bay, where its thickness is 66 feet.

Altogether some 16 subdivisions have been recognized near Atherfield, but for general purposes the following four-fold division is used:—

Carstone
Sandrock Series
Ferruginous Sands
Atherfield Clay (with the *Perna* Bed at base)

Many fossils are found in the *Perna* Bed in addition to *Mulletia* [*Perna*] *mulleti*. They include the coral *Holocystis elegans*, the brachiopod *Sellithyris sella*, several species of the bivalved shells *Arca* and *Trigonia*, frequent examples of *Panopea* in the position of life, and the large oyster-like *Exogyra latissima* (=*E. sinuata*). The overlying Atherfield Clay (80 ft), a light-blue silty clay with numerous flat clay-ironstone nodules, yields very few fossils. Above the Atherfield Clay, and often grouped with it on account of similar lithology, is the highly fossiliferous Lower Lobster Bed (25 to 30 ft). It is so named because of the frequent occurrence of the small lobster *Meyeria vectensis*; the crab *Mithracites vectensis* and the sea-urchin *Toxaster renevieri* are also found in this bed, as are numerous examples of the ammonite *Deshayesites*.

The next division, the Ferruginous Sands, is about 500 ft in thickness and includes clayey grit, dark-green sands full of glauconite, sands and clays, with layers of concretions and fossiliferous nodules here and there. In it also are several beds of ferruginous sandstone, with polished and often oolitic brown grains. This division is the equivalent of the Hythe Beds and the Sandgate Beds of south-eastern England. An interesting part of the series, near the base, is the Crackers Group (20 ft), of coarse grey and brown sand which contains two layers of massive concretions, which are popularly known as ' crackers ' in some parts of the country. Many fossils are contained in the concretions; among the commonest are the bivalved shells *Gervillella sublanceolata* and *Thetironia minor*, the univalved shell *Natica rotundata* and ammonites of the genus *Deshayesites*, especially *Deshayesites deshayesi*. Higher up in the Ferruginous Sands are divisons named mostly after the characteristic fossils. Thus the upper part of the Crackers Group is the Upper Lobster Bed (40 ft) yielding *Meyeria vectensis*. Above is the Lower *Gryphaea* Bed (33 ft) named after the large and thick oyster-like shell *Exogyra latissima*, which occurs in bands and was first thought to be a *Gryphaea*. Other beds named after fossils are the ' *Scaphites* Group ' (50 ft), with the loosely-coiled ammonoid shell *Australiceras* [*Scaphites*] *gigas* and

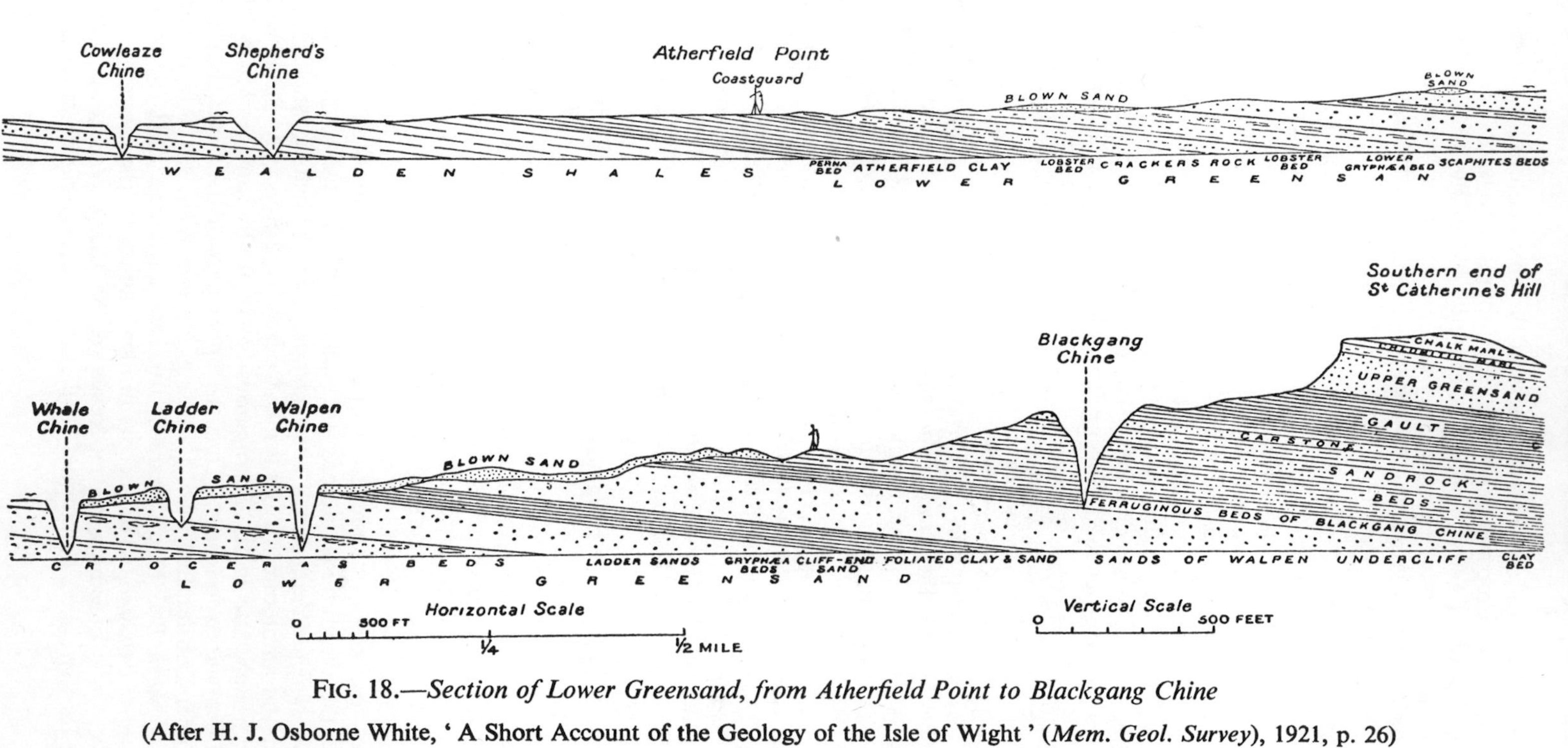

FIG. 18.—*Section of Lower Greensand, from Atherfield Point to Blackgang Chine*

(After H. J. Osborne White, ' A Short Account of the Geology of the Isle of Wight ' (*Mem. Geol. Survey*), 1921, p. 26)

A. LULWORTH COVE AND STAIR HOLE, DORSET

B. FOSSIL FOREST, EAST OF LULWORTH COVE

(*For details see p.* iv)

A. CHALK SCENERY NEAR ASKERSWELL, DORSET

B. CRETACEOUS-JURASSIC UNCONFORMITY AT WHITE NOTHE, DORSET
(*For details see p.* iv)

the Lower and Upper '*Crioceras* Groups' (16 ft and 46 ft) with *Tropaeum*. Between the last two groups are the Walpen Sands and Clay (57 ft). Above the Upper *Crioceras* Group are the Walpen and Ladder Sands (42 ft) and then another series with bands of *Exogyra latissima*, the Upper *Gryphaea* Group (16 ft). The remaining divisions of the Ferruginous Sands, in upward order of succession, are the Cliff End Sands (28 ft), the Foliated Clay and Sand (25 ft), the Sands of Walpen Undercliff (97 ft) and the Ferruginous Sands of Blackgang Chine (20 ft).

On the coast the Ferruginous Sands form bold cliffs, cut into here and there by chines; Blackgang Chine is the best known of these (Fig. 18).

The Sandrock Series, equivalent to the Folkestone Beds of south-eastern England, consists of beds of quartz-sand, white, yellow or grey in colour, and slightly coherent; occasional laminae of clay and lines of small pebbles are also included. The thickness is variable, being 184 ft near Blackgang Chine, but less than 100 ft on the east and west of the island. On account of the pervious nature of these beds fossils are very rarely preserved. After the deposition of the Sandrock Series there was probably a pause in sedimentation and some erosion before the overlying Carstone was laid down, for there are traces of a phosphatic pebble bed at its base.

The Carstone consists of coarse brown sand and grit, with scattered quartzite pebbles and lines of iron oxide; when unweathered it is of an olive-green colour. Although the Carstone is regarded as the top division of the Lower Greensand in this area its inclusion in that formation is based on lithology, for the few imperfectly-preserved fossils that have been found bear more resemblance to those of the next higher formation—the Gault.

In the Isle of Wight there are fairly complete coast-sections in Compton Bay, at Atherfield and at Redcliff, as well as the long sections on the southern coast of the island between Atherfield and Sandown.

The detailed subdivisions of the Lower Greensand that have been noted in the Atherfield area cannot be readily determined throughout the Isle of Wight; and on the eastern end of the Purbeck peninsula not even the four main divisions can be identified. The formation thins out at Mupe Bay and is seen no farther west.

Inland the Lower Greensand is exposed in small isolated areas. A narrow outcrop south of Shaftesbury extends for about 6 miles along the border of the Gault. The thickness here does not exceed 40 ft, and the formation comprises beds of sand, clay, glauconitic and sandy clays, with occasional mottling. In the absence of fossils it is not possible to refer these beds to any particular subdivision.

In the Vale of Wardour the Lower Greensand is represented by 15 or 20 ft of glauconitic sand with occasional traces of chert, but the outcrop is unimportant and exposures few. A wider outcrop with a few outliers extends west and north-west of Devizes, where the formation includes ferruginous sands, sandy loams and ironstones. A small outlier caps the hill at Seend, and there the beds include an ironstone that was formerly quarried, the ore being smelted on the spot. The beds here have yielded a large number of fossils, including the ammonite *Parahoplites nutfieldensis* and many shells of brachiopods and molluscs.

Farther north, near Calne, is another small outcrop, of a variable thickness but less than 40 feet. Here the beds are ferruginous sands and sandstones with subordinate clay-seams, bands of pebbles and occasional lenses of white sand. The fossils are mostly casts and moulds of bivalved shells and brachiopods, among them the peculiar lamellibranch *Toucasia lonsdalei*.

These inland outcrops of the Lower Greensand show clearly that the formation in this part of the country was laid down by a transgressive sea. Earth-movements had brought certain of the Upper Jurassic strata within the range of marine erosion. As a result in different parts in this inland area the Portland, Purbeck and Wealden beds have been planed away before or during the transgression of this sea. In various localities therefore the Lower Greensand rests successively on the Wealden Beds, the Purbeck Beds, the Portland Beds and the Kimmeridge Clay (as in the Vale of Wardour).

GAULT AND UPPER GREENSAND

A further downward movement followed the deposition of the Lower Greensand, a movement more rapid and extensive than that which submerged the area over which the Wealden beds were deposited. There was also a slight general tilting towards the east and uplift towards the west, so that the sea as it swept westwards, eroding as it went, spread its deposits on successively older strata; these deposits (the Gault and Upper Greensand) overstep all the Jurassic formations until they rest on the Trias, beyond the western borders of our area. This can be seen when the outcrop is traced from the Vale of Wardour to near Lyme Regis. Near Lyme Regis the Gault and Upper Greensand can be seen resting successively on Middle Lias (as on Golden Cap), the Middle and Lower Lias junction (as on Stonebarrow) and on the Lower Lias (as on Black Ven).

The Gault and Upper Greensand must be regarded as variations of one formation. The former name is used when the deposits are mostly clays; the latter when sandy beds predominate; but the fossils prove that clay-beds in one part of the country are of the same age as sandy developments elsewhere. Where both types occur the Upper Greensand facies overlies the clay facies. In general terms the sandy element becomes more conspicuous as the formation is traced westwards, until near Lyme Regis the Gault is not only thin but sandy, while the Upper Greensand is a much more prominent development. Fossils of all groups are found in this formation; and species of ammonites, by reason of their restricted vertical range, provide a means of subdivision into zones. By means of the ammonites, also, beds in different parts of the country can be correlated irrespective of their lithic character.

FIG. 19.—*Fossils from the Wealden Beds and the Lower Greensand.*

1. *Sellithyris sella* (J. de C. Sowerby); 2. *Sulcirhynchia hythensis* (E. Owen); 3. *Thetironia minor* (J. Sowerby); 4. *Cassiope lujani* (de Loriol); 5. *Mulletia* [*Perna*] *mulleti* (Deshayes); 6. *Deshayesites deshayesi* (Auctt); 7. *Cypridea tuberculata* (J. de C. Sowerby); 8. *Metacypris fittoni* (Mantell); 9. *Cypridea valdensis* (J. de C. Sowerby); 10. *Cypridea spinigera* (J. de C. Sowerby); 11. *Nemocardium* (*Pratulum*) *ibbetsoni* (Forbes); 12. *Viviparus sp.* 13. *Unio valdensis* Mantell; 14. *Paraglauconia strombiformis* (Schlotheim), var. *tricarinata* (J. de C. Sowerby).

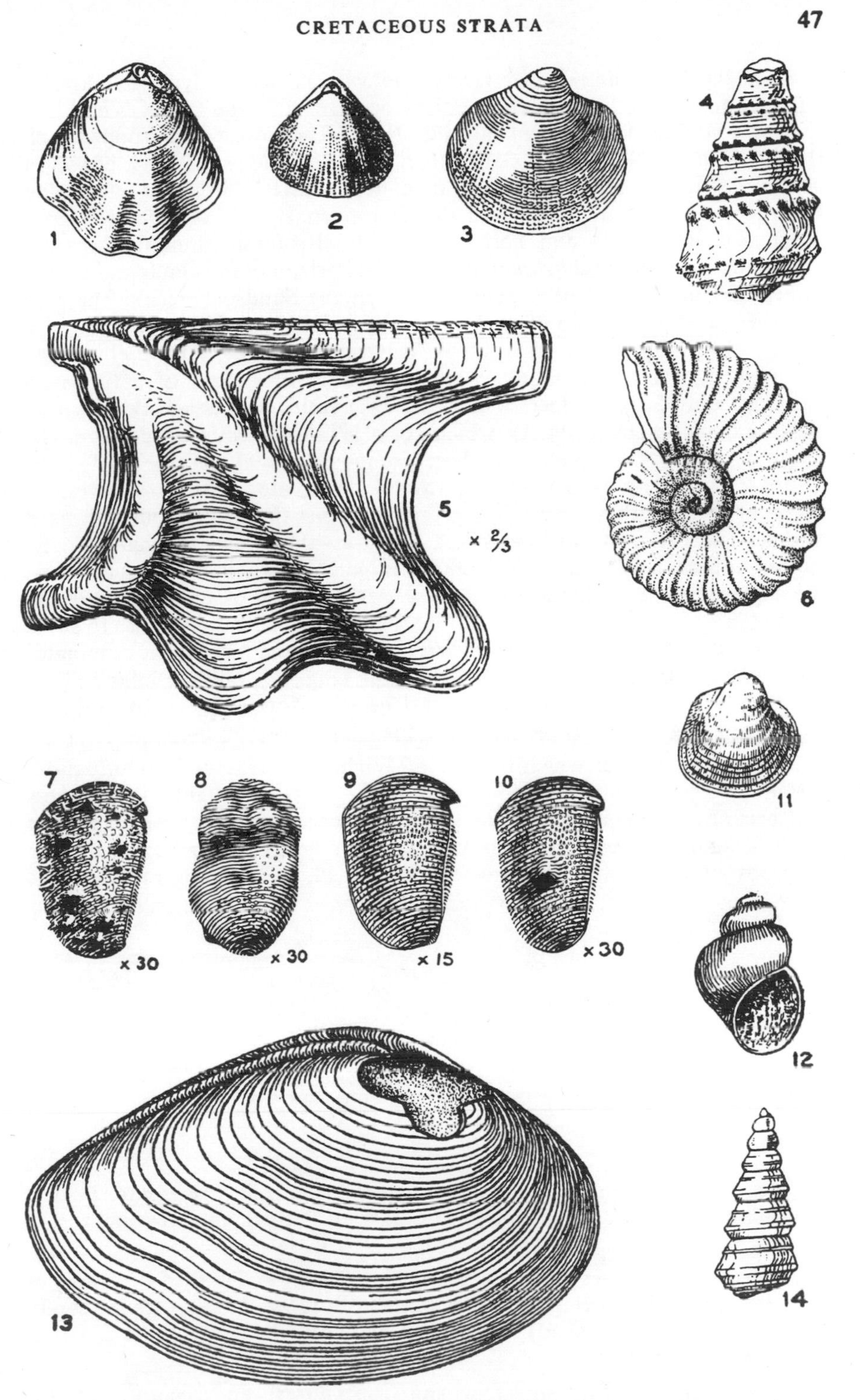

FIG. 19.—*Fossils from the Wealden Beds and the Lower Greensand*

Since the Gault and Upper Greensand vary considerably in our area it will be appropriate first to describe their occurrence in the Isle of Wight and then to trace the development in other areas. The lowest bed grouped with the Gault in the island is the Carstone, a coarse sand or sandstone, brown in colour. This bed becomes thicker in a north-easterly direction, increasing from a few inches at Punfield on the Dorset coast, 6 ft at Compton Bay, 30 ft near Bonchurch and 72 ft at Redcliff. Its fossils, among them the ammonite *Beudanticeras ligatum*, indicate the horizon of the Gault and Lower Greensand junction. The Carstone rests on the Sandrock series, but here and there a basement bed of pebbles and occasional fossils derived from the Lower Greensand point to a break between the two. Above, it passes gradually upwards into Gault, which is mostly blue clay, of a thickness varying from 95 to 103 feet. Then follows a series of Passage Beds, sandy clays and marls (15 to 44 ft), which form a lithological passage from the Gault to the Upper Greensand, here composed mainly of speckled, light greenish to blue-grey sandstones. Small chocolate-coloured concretions occur in most of these beds. At certain horizons the beds abound in hard nodules (cornstones); on weathered surfaces these give a characteristic rugged appearance. Some beds contain large concretions or doggers, while the higher beds are characterized by a development of chert in scattered concretions and in regular courses. The Upper Greensand gives rise to some conspicuous features in the Isle of Wight, such as the cliff which dominates the Undercliff from Bonchurch to Blackgang (Fig. 23), and the inland bluffs of the Southern Downs. In the central range it forms the scarp of Rams Down and hog-backed ridges south of the Chalk near Brading.

In South Dorset, of which the Isle of Wight is a structural continuation, certain changes are observable in the Gault. It increases slightly in thickness and becomes dissociated from the Lower Cretaceous beds on which it rests in the Island, and passes across the Wealden beds and thence across the outcrops of the Upper Jurassic formations (Pl. VII B, and Fig. 20). Its

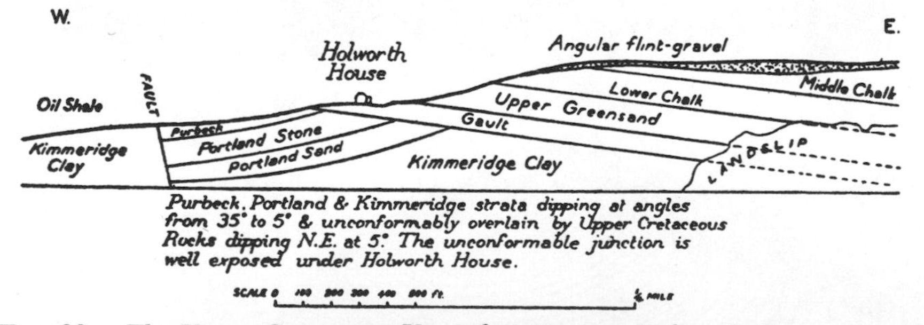

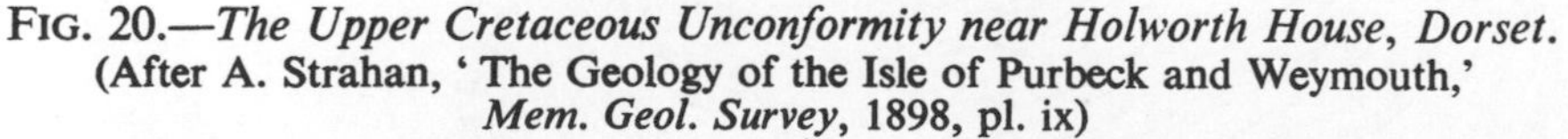

FIG. 20.—*The Upper Cretaceous Unconformity near Holworth House, Dorset.* (After A. Strahan, 'The Geology of the Isle of Purbeck and Weymouth,' *Mem. Geol. Survey*, 1898, pl. ix)

lithic character changes also; the Gault clay (91 ft) at Punfield decreases in thickness westwards, being 40 ft at Ringstead Bay, while the overlying sandy beds (the Upper Greensand) increase in thickness. In places there is a thin pebbly basement bed.

The separation of the Gault from the Upper Greensand becomes increasingly difficult as we proceed westward in South Dorset, since the Gault becomes more sandy in that direction than it is in the eastern part of our area. At the south-western end of the district large tracts of Gault and Upper Greensand are detached from the main outcrop of Upper Cretaceous strata and occur as isolated areas (outliers) occupying the highest points, *e.g.* Pilsdon Pen, Lewesdon Hill and Hardown Hill. Near the coast these Upper Cretaceous beds form the cappings of Black Ven, Stonebarrow and Golden Cap. On Black Ven, the Gault, with a thin basement bed containing derived fossils from the Lias, is represented by dark blue loam and sand (24 ft). Fossils from the Gault here include bivalved shells (*Inoceramus concentricus*, *Panopea gurgitis* and *Pinna robinaldina*), univalved shells (*Perissoptera marginata* and *Gyrodes genti*), echinoids (*Hemiaster asterias*), and the ammonite *Anahoplites praecox*. Tubes of the marine worm *Rotularia concava* are common. Above the Gault the Upper Greensand is represented by grey sands with layers of 'Cowstones' (20 ft), 'Foxmould' (74 ft) and Chert Beds (20 ft, much shattered). The Cowstones, oval masses of calcareous sandstone, were so named from a fancied resemblance to cattle of the fallen blocks that lie on the slopes bordering the coast. They are of concretionary origin, having been formed by the segregation of calcium carbonate, derived from calcareous organisms that have been dissolved by percolating water. Fossils are fairly frequent in the Cowstones, and include the lobster *Homarus longimanus*, the bivalved shells *Grammatodon carinatus*, *Exogyra conica* and *Entolium orbiculare*. A fragment of the ammonite *Mortoniceras* has also been found. Foxmould is a local name for a brown and grey sand, which in its lower part is loamy and contains concretions. Silicified shells occur in local patches, and casts of shells are present in the sands. Among the fossils recorded from the Foxmould are *Rotularia concava*, *Exogyra conica* and the marginally folded oyster-shell *Lopha diluviana*. Between the Foxmould and the Chert Beds are 6 ft of rusty sands with broken shells of '*Pecten*.' The succession of the beds of Gault and Upper Greensand on Stonebarrow and Golden Cap varies in detail.

The main outcrop can be traced from near Abbotsbury as a sinuous band to Mosterton, where it swings in a general easterly direction and then northeastwards until it enters the Vale of Wardour. To the east of Beaminster the Upper Greensand has a thickness of 100 ft, although it is much thicker in the south. The lowest beds consist of fine clayey sands containing in the western part large lenticular masses of compact grey calcareous sandstone like the cowstones of Lyme Regis. These beds pass up into soft grey sands and then into greenish sands which are surmounted by 2 or 3 ft of rubbly glauconitic sandstone. Above this is a bed of greensand which passes up gradually into a calcareous grit; in places this forms a feature in the topography and has been quarried at several localities near Maiden Newton. Between Beaminster and Maiden Newton the top of the grit contains broken fossils belonging to the base of the next higher formation (the Chalk), and its upper surface is eroded. Evidently in this neighbourhood there were passage beds between the two formations, and these were broken up when the lowest beds of the Chalk were deposited. In this neighbourhood also layers and nodules of chert are developed in the Upper Greensand.

North of Maiden Newton, near Evershot, the strike of the Gault and Upper Greensand runs in a general direction from west to east until it turns north-eastwards across the valley of the Stour into the Vale of Wardour. The Gault thins out west of Evershot but increases to 60 ft near Shillingstone consisting chiefly of sandy glauconite clays. The Upper Greensand varies in thickness along this outcrop, being 60 to 70 ft near Okeford Fitzpaine and increasing westwards. Most of it is soft sand with occasional doggers, but towards the west a bed of rubbly glauconitic sandstone comes in at the top. Towards Shaftesbury the Gault (90 ft) can be traced as a continuous band of yellow, brown and grey micaceous clays below the escarpment of the Upper Greensand. The Upper Greensand here increases to 150 ft in thickness and comprises the following divisions: (at the top) fine greensand (10 ft), chert beds (20 ft), coarse glauconitic sandstone (10 ft), soft grey and buff sand (70 ft), micaceous sands and sandstone (40 ft).

A conspicuous topographic feature is formed by the glauconitic sandstone, and the chert beds give rise to an escarpment. In the neighbourhood of Shaftesbury are many overgrown quarries where a hard glauconitic sandstone (the ' Rag ') was used for road metal and a softer variety with a calcite cement was worked as a building stone. At the southern end of the Vale of Wardour the Upper Greensand forms a high plateau from 700 to 800 ft above O.D. The outcrop of the Gault and Upper Greensand to the north of Shaftesbury is very irregular on account of the flexures that gave rise to the Vales of Wardour, Warminster and Pewsey. In the Vale of Wardour the clay and sandy facies are present on both the north and south sides of the Vale, the dip being slight on the south and steep on the north. The Gault (with a thin bed of quartz and lydite pebbles at its base) is a dark grey micaceous silty clay with numerous phosphatic nodules (90 ft). It passes up into an impure Malmstone, a fine-grained siliceous rock, which in turn merges gradually into soft sands. The higher members of the Upper Greensand series consist first of a massive calcareous sandstone; above are soft grey silty sands with lenticular layers of chert, and finally gritty green sand.

North of the Vale of Wardour the Gault maintains a thickness of 70 to 90 ft, but the thickness of the Upper Greensand varies and diminishes considerably past the Vale of Warminster. The Gault is succeeded by the Malmstone (15 to 25 ft), which passes up into soft micaceous sandstone or ' gaize '; in places this is indurated so as to form a line of doggers or ' burrstones.' These burr-stones, some of them 2½ ft by 1½ ft, contain fossils, among them tubes of the marine worm *Rotularia concava* and the bivalved shells *Entolium orbiculare*, *Neithea quinquecostata*, and *Exogyra conica*.

The uppermost beds in this part of Wiltshire are the Warminster Beds, which comprise three divisions: 1 (at the base), greensands with layers of glauconitic limestone; 2, chert beds, fine greyish sands with sponge-spicules and layers of chert and siliceous stone; 3, green sand with nodules and layers of calcareous stone. The chert beds have yielded complete ' skeletons '

FIG. 21.—*Fossils from the Gault and the Upper Greensand*

1. *Neithea quadricostata* (J. Sowerby); 2. *Dentalium decussatum* J. Sowerby; 3. *Holaster fossarius* (Benett); 4. *Entolium orbiculare* (J. Sowerby); 5. *Chlamys* (*Aequipecten*) *aspera* (Lamarck); 6. *Exogyra conica* (J. Sowerby); 7. *Inoceramus concentricus* Parkinson; 8. *Rotularia concava* (J. Sowerby); 9. *Inoceramus sulcatus* Parkinson; 10. *Acila* (*Truncacila*) *bivirgata* (J. Sowerby); 11. *Hysteroceras varicosum* (J. de C. Sowerby); 12. *Nucula ovata* Mantell.

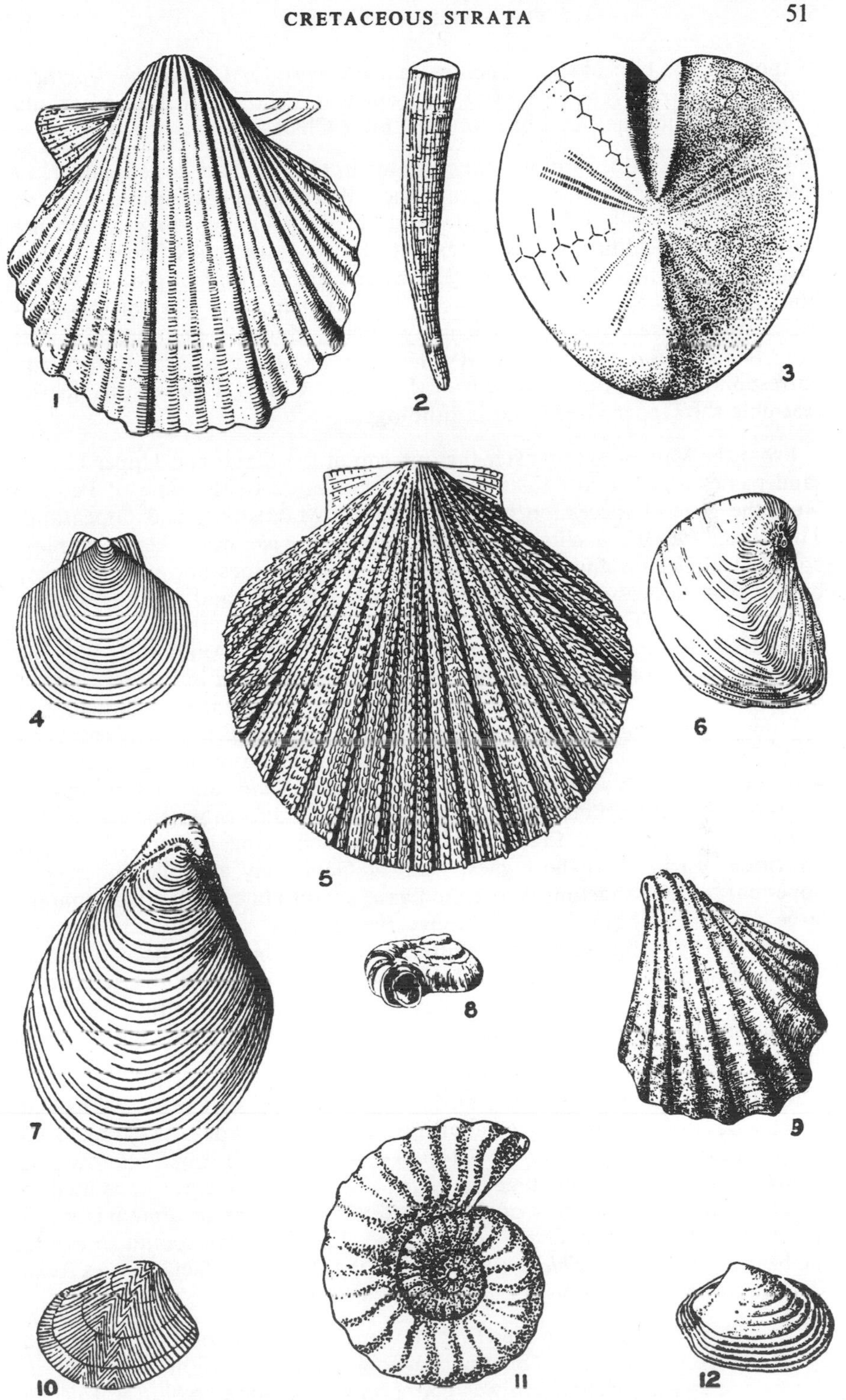

FIG. 21.—*Fossils from the Gault and the Upper Greensand*

of sponges, the typical species being *Hallirhoa costata*, *Doryderma benettiae*, and *Pachypoterion robustum*. The fossils of Bed 3 show that this bed should be included with the basal beds of the Lower Chalk.

Through the industry of a local collector in bygone days large numbers of fossils were labelled as coming from the 'Warminster Greensand.' In the early days of fossil collecting, however, accuracy in recording the precise horizons and localities of fossils was not observed; and subsequent study of fossils from the neighbourhood of Warminster has shown that more than one horizon and locality are represented. It is evident that most of these so-called Warminster fossils (particularly small echinoids and brachiopods) came from the Rye Hill Sands of Rye Hill Farm and Shute Farm, the horizon corresponding with the basal beds of the Lower Chalk, which in this district resemble the Upper Greensand in lithology.

From the Vale of Warminster the outcrop of the Gault and Upper Greensand passes as a narrow tract east-north-eastwards to the Vale of Pewsey. Here the general succession comprises Gault, Malmstone, and Greensand. The Gault (90 ft), a silty micaceous clay, yellowish near the base, lilac-coloured higher up and grey and sandy at the top, does not enter the Vale but indents the western margin and passes northwards and north-eastwards out of our area. The Malmstone (10 to 16 ft) is similar to that farther south, and passes up into micaceous sandstone (30 to 40 ft). Ammonites are the principal fossils of the Gault, but represent species found only in the lowest beds at the type-section at Folkestone, while the Malmstone is characterized by tubes of the marine worm *Rotularia concava* and the bivalved shell *Aucellina gryphaeoides*. Fossils are fairly common in the micaceous sandstone, and include the bivalved shells *Panopea mandibula* and *Grammatodon carinatus*, and the ammonites *Callihoplites patella* and other species of this genus. The ammonites found in the sandy facies (the Upper Greensand) are those restricted to the highest beds of Gault clay at Folkestone. The upper part of the sandstone is soft and passes up into fine sands which contain large doggers or 'burr-stones.' Above the sands is a continuous layer of hard grey sandy limestone (the Potterne Rock), which has been quarried for building stone, and contains fossils similar to those of the sandstone below. The Greensand division above consists of glauconitic sand with several courses of greenish calcareous sandstone (30 ft), but this becomes thinner north of Devizes.

In places the glauconitic beds at the top of the Upper Greensand extend into the base of the overlying Chalk formation. These beds are characterized by the bivalved shell *Chlamys* (*Aequipecten*) *aspera*, formerly known as *Pecten asper*, and for some time the term 'Zone of *Pecten asper*' was used to denote them. A close study of the occurrence of species of ammonites has since shown that the upper part of this so-called zone corresponds in age to the base of the Chalk. *Chlamys* (*Aequipecten*) *aspera* is, in fact, a facies fossil and cannot therefore be used as an exact index of age.

The end of the time when the Upper Greensand was deposited was marked by a change in conditions on the sea-floor. Current-action was then in progress, and while deposition was going on in one place erosion was active in another. Consequently the junction with the overlying Chalk formation

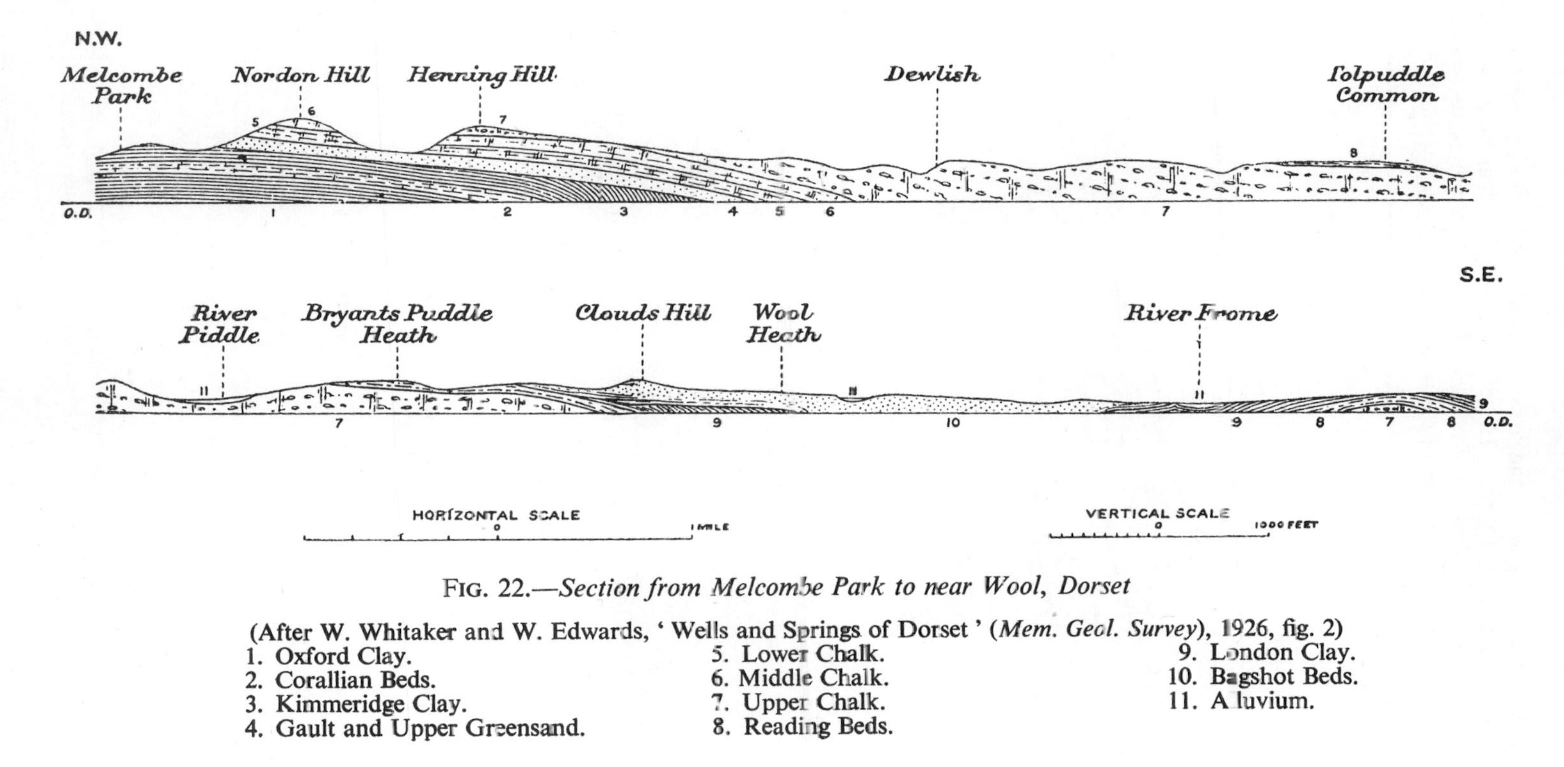

FIG. 22.—*Section from Melcombe Park to near Wool, Dorset*

(After W. Whitaker and W. Edwards, 'Wells and Springs of Dorset' (*Mem. Geol. Survey*), 1926, fig. 2)

1. Oxford Clay.
2. Corallian Beds.
3. Kimmeridge Clay.
4. Gault and Upper Greensand.
5. Lower Chalk.
6. Middle Chalk.
7. Upper Chalk.
8. Reading Beds.
9. London Clay.
10. Bagshot Beds.
11. Alluvium.

varies in different parts of the area. Passage beds, present in South Wiltshire, are not seen in Dorset. In general some few feet of glauconitic and sandy beds were laid down as the base of the Lower Chalk before the comparatively tranquil conditions of chalk-deposition were established.

e. Chert Beds. *d.* Freestones. *c.* Sandstones with concretions.
Lower Chalk appears in the slope above the cliff.

FIG. 23.—*Sketch of the Upper Greensand escarpment in the Undercliff near Niton, Isle of Wight*

(After H. J. Osborne White, 'A Short Account of the Geology of the Isle of Wight' (*Mem. Geol. Survey*), 1921, p. 56)

THE CHALK

This is the most familiar formation in the south-east of England; it occupies the greater part of the area here included with the Hampshire Basin and its total thickness is more than 1,600 ft (Pl. I). The Chalk is entirely of marine origin, but only in the lowest beds is there any considerable trace of detrital constituents; the bulk of the formation is remarkable on account of the absence of terrigenous material. This may be partly due to land areas being far distant and partly to the prevalence of desert conditions on the land at that time. Temporary shallowing of the sea took place occasionally, as shown by evidence of current action (*e.g.* the Chalk Rock) and of certain fossils. Different opinions have been held as to the nature and origin of the Chalk. At one time it was regarded as a deep-sea deposit comparable with the Globigerina ooze of the Atlantic; and some investigators have thought it to be a chemical precipitate, while others have contended that bacterial action was a considerable factor in its formation. The constitution of the Chalk has recently been under investigation by Mr. Maurice Black, with results that seem to have met with general acceptance. The facts now adduced agree better with a theory of primarily organic origin than with one invoking purely inorganic processes. Chalk varies considerably in constitution according to the proportion of the various components, the many varieties including the common soft chalks, gritty but friable chalk, and hard or nodular rock. Ordinary white chalk is a mixture of fine material (coccoliths, the excessively minute calcareous bodies produced by planktonic algae, and their disintegration products) and a varying proportion of shell-debris and foraminifera, the coarser fragments being embedded in a matrix of coccolith material. Coccoliths are present in vast numbers and in all stages of disintegration down to individual component crystals. The electron microscope shows that the finest particles of the matrix are of the same order of size as the individual crystals of the associated coccoliths, and the shape of the grains also varies with horizon according to the prevalent type of coccolith. Modern precipitated oozes, in contrast, contain scarcely any trace of coccoliths and relatively little shell material, their finer fractions having an abundance of minute aragonite crystals. Microscopic examination of chalk from certain horizons also shows a large proportion of minute spherical bodies called 'spheres.' These 'spheres' are presumably organic structures, but their exact nature is problematical; where they are abundant the chalk is apt to be rather hard or nodular.

Three main divisions of the Chalk are recognized—Lower, Middle and Upper; these are distinguishable not only by lithic characters but also by the fossils. Many fossils have a definite range in the Chalk, and can be used as indexes to the successive stages of the animal population of the sea on the bed of which the Chalk was deposited. The three main divisions can thus be subdivided, by means of the fossils, into a series of zones.

Lower Chalk.—At the base of this division in Wiltshire and the Isle of Wight are passage beds from the Upper Greensand. These beds are well seen in the neighbourhood of Maiden Bradley and Mere, in Wiltshire (Fig. 24) where a bed with concretions (the Cornstones, or Popple Bed) marks the approximate base. Actually the sand beneath the Cornstones sometimes contains the same fossils as are found in the Cornstones, and the strict line of division would therefore be within that bed. Among the fossils of the Cornstones and Popple Bed are the echinoid *Catopygus columbarius*, numerous brachiopods including '*Terebratula*' *dutempleana*, *Terebrirostra lyra* and '*Rhynchonella*' *dimidiata*, shells of lamellibranchs, and the ammonites, *Hyphoplites falcatus*, and *Mantelliceras saxbii*.

In some places a small thickness of glauconitic sand with phosphatic lumps and numerous fossils succeeds the Cornstones, but the next important bed is the Chloritic Marl. This bed (1 ft 6 in.-12 ft), which usually marks the base of the Chalk in the south of England, varies from dark-green glauconitic marly sand and sandstone to light-grey sandy marl; it contains phosphatic concretions and abundant fossils, including many species that are found in the Cornstones. The sponge *Stauronema carteri* is conspicuous among the fossils, which include the bivalved shell *Chlamys* (*Aequipecten*) *aspera* and the echinoid *Holaster fossarius*. Although called Chloritic Marl the mineral chlorite is not present, glauconite having been mistaken for it; but the term Chloritic Marl is still retained for this stratal subdivision.

Above this bed the main mass of the Lower Chalk consists of the Chalk Marl and the Grey Chalk. The Chalk Marl varies in thickness up to 100 ft, and is mostly a bluish-grey or buff marly chalk. It is characterized by ammonites of the genera *Schloenbachia*, *Calycoceras* and *Mantelliceras*, bivalved shells including *Chlamys* (*Aequipecten*) *beaveri* and *Inoceramus crippsi*, and tubes of the worm *Serpula umbonata*. In the Isle of Wight the sponge *Plocoscyphia labrosa* is particularly common near the base. Occasionally grey flinty lumps with a core of black flint are found in the Chalk Marl. The Grey Chalk, which in places attains a thickness of more than 100 ft, consists of pale grey or yellowish-white slightly marly chalk, massively bedded. Its fossils include the oyster *Ostrea vesicularis*, and other bivalved shells such as *Plicatula inflata* and *Inoceramus tenuis*, the echinoids *Holaster subglobosus* and *H. trecensis*, tubes of the worm *Serpula ampullacea* and of *Terebella lewesiensis*, a much larger worm, that had its integument formed largely of detached fish-scales. Ammonites of the genus *Acanthoceras* are common in this division, as are also *Turrilites* and *Scaphites*. In the Vale of Pewsey there is a bed (14 ft) of soft, whitish siliceous chalk with numerous flinty concretions. The concretions are flinty or cherty nodules of irregular shape, bluish-grey when broken, and are quite different from ordinary chalk flints.

The upper limit of the Lower Chalk is marked by the *plenus* Marls (2 to 6 ft), comprising greenish-grey marly bands with layers of lighter chalk. These marls are characterized by the belemnite *Actinocamax plenus*.

Middle Chalk.—This division varies in thickness up to 200 ft, although not much more than half that amount in places. The beds near the base have a distinctly nodular structure, being sometimes hard and white and sometimes with slightly yellow nodules and lumps in pale grey streaky marl. Over most of the area a definite basal rock-bed is thus recognized—the Melbourn Rock (1 to 14 ft), but this is not distinctly developed in South Dorset and the Isle of Wight. Above, the chalk becomes firm, white and homogeneous, with partings here and there of thin layers of marl. Flints occur as scattered nodules or in layers. There are no flints in the Middle Chalk of the Isle of Wight, but near the top of this division there are two bands of siliceous nodules which look like flints but have the texture of chalk. In places, *e.g.* north of the Vale of Pewsey and in the Isle of Wight, the upper part of the Middle Chalk becomes lumpy and nodular and a conspicuous band of yellowish chalk with green-coated nodules is developed. This band in the Isle of Wight has been called the 'Spurious Chalk Rock.'

The commonest fossils of the Middle Chalk are brachiopod shells, echinoids and bivalved shells. Two small species of brachiopods are characteristic; one, a globose, plainly-ribbed form (*Orbirhynchia cuvieri*) is typical

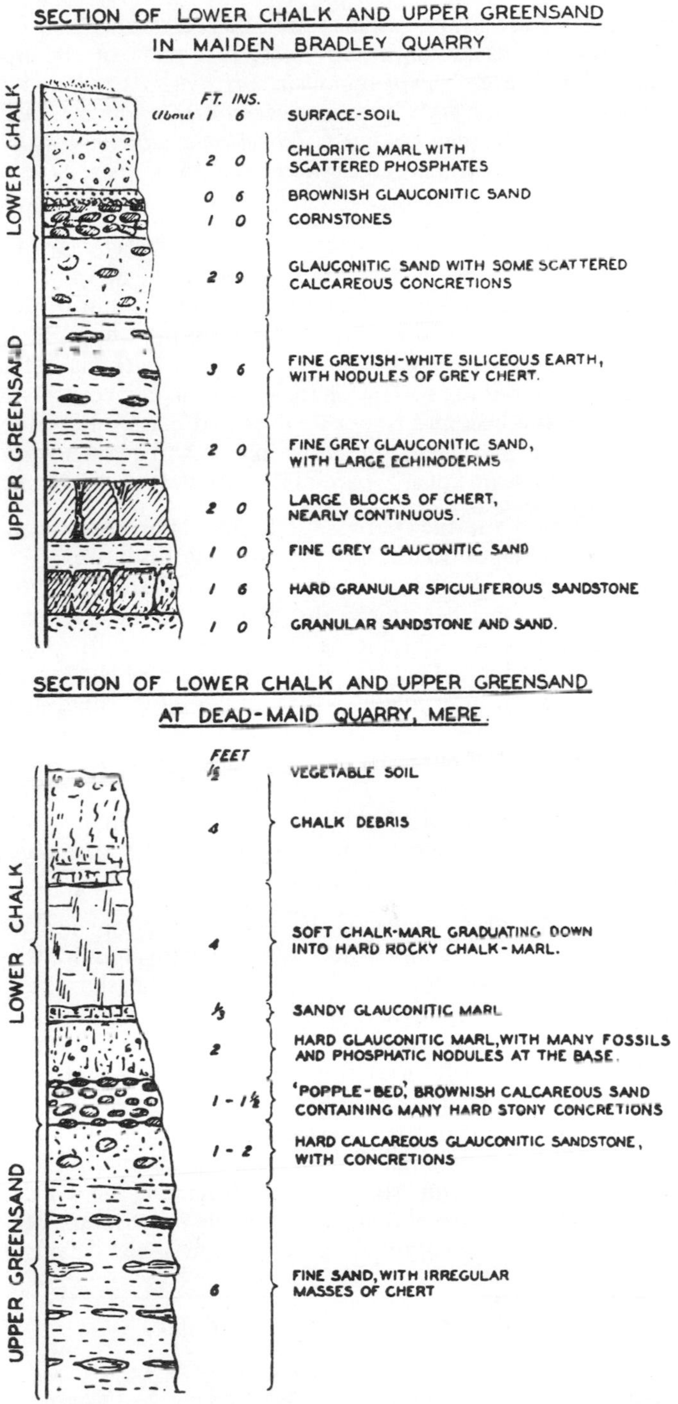

SECTION OF LOWER CHALK AND UPPER GREENSAND IN MAIDEN BRADLEY QUARRY

	FT.	INS.	
	About 1	6	SURFACE-SOIL
LOWER CHALK	2	0	CHLORITIC MARL WITH SCATTERED PHOSPHATES
	0	6	BROWNISH GLAUCONITIC SAND
	1	0	CORNSTONES
UPPER GREENSAND	2	9	GLAUCONITIC SAND WITH SOME SCATTERED CALCAREOUS CONCRETIONS
	3	6	FINE GREYISH-WHITE SILICEOUS EARTH, WITH NODULES OF GREY CHERT.
	2	0	FINE GREY GLAUCONITIC SAND, WITH LARGE ECHINODERMS
	2	0	LARGE BLOCKS OF CHERT, NEARLY CONTINUOUS.
	1	0	FINE GREY GLAUCONITIC SAND
	1	6	HARD GRANULAR SPICULIFEROUS SANDSTONE
	1	0	GRANULAR SANDSTONE AND SAND.

SECTION OF LOWER CHALK AND UPPER GREENSAND AT DEAD-MAID QUARRY, MERE.

	FEET	
LOWER CHALK	½	VEGETABLE SOIL
	4	CHALK DEBRIS
	4	SOFT CHALK-MARL GRADUATING DOWN INTO HARD ROCKY CHALK-MARL.
	⅓	SANDY GLAUCONITIC MARL
	2	HARD GLAUCONITIC MARL, WITH MANY FOSSILS AND PHOSPHATIC NODULES AT THE BASE.
	1 - 1½	'POPPLE-BED', BROWNISH CALCAREOUS SAND CONTAINING MANY HARD STONY CONCRETIONS
UPPER GREENSAND	1 - 2	HARD CALCAREOUS GLAUCONITIC SANDSTONE, WITH CONCRETIONS
	6	FINE SAND, WITH IRREGULAR MASSES OF CHERT

FIG. 24.—*Sections showing the junction of the Upper Greensand and Lower Chalk in Wiltshire*

(Adapted from A. J. Jukes-Browne and J. Scanes, *Quart. Journ. Geol. Soc.*, vol. lvii, 1901, pp. 101 and 111)

of the lower part of the Middle Chalk; the other, a smaller and flatter form with fine divergent ribs (*Terebratulina lata*) is typical of the upper part. Among the echinoids are *Conulus castanea*, *Discoidea dixoni*, and *Hemiaster (Peroniaster) nasutulus*, formerly known as *Hemiaster minimus*. Two common species of bivalved shells may be noted: *Inoceramus labiatus* restricted to the lower part, and *I. lamarcki*, characteristic of the upper part.

Upper Chalk.—Most of the Chalk in the area belongs to this division, which in the Isle of Wight attains a thickness of 1,326 feet. In most places its base is marked by a nodular bed, the Chalk Rock, of varying thickness up to 8 feet. Sometimes this bed is conspicuous on account of the presence of green-coated nodules. In other parts of England the Chalk Rock contains a peculiar assemblage of fossils, mostly mollusca, but this assemblage is poorly represented in our area. The Chalk above this bed loses its rough and nodular character and becomes smooth, white and massively bedded. Flints occur throughout, in nodular form, sometimes set in regular courses or in tabular seams. Thin seams of marl are also present at certain horizons.

Fossils are common and the species numerous, each zonal division having its distinctive assemblage. In the lower zones the echinoid *Micraster* (the 'heart-urchin') is distinctive, and certain parts of its shell (or 'test') show progressive modification when traced through successively higher horizons; higher up, detached plates of crinoids (*Uintacrinus* and *Marsupites*) mark distinctive horizons of limited extent. Then come beds of chalk characterized by the small echinoid *Offaster pilula*. Higher still are two zones distinguished by species of belemnites; first is that of *Gonioteuthis quadrata*, and above, denoting the highest division of the Chalk in this part of the country, is the zone of *Belemnitella mucronata*. The echinoid *Echinocorys scutata* ranges throughout the Upper Chalk and exhibits variations in shape that generally correspond with horizon; one form in particular, the var. *depressula*, is restricted to the lower part of the Chalk with *Offaster pilula*.

Most of the principal divisions of the animal kingdom are represented among the fossils of the Chalk, which number many hundreds. Remains of fishes occur usually as isolated teeth, those of the sharks *Lamna* and *Scapanorhynchus* and crushing teeth of the ray *Ptychodus* being the most common. Ammonites are frequent in the lower part of the Chalk and have been useful for purposes of correlation. In the Middle and Upper Chalk they are too infrequent in occurrence to be used as a means of subdivision. Gastropods also are found in the lowest beds, and among the genera represented are *Aporrhais*, *Pleurotomaria*, *Solarium*, and *Trochus*. Lamellibranch shells are very common and are found throughout the Chalk: *Ostrea*, *Chlamys* and *Spondylus* are well represented, while *Inoceramus*, besides being the most frequent shell, is of zonal value, certain species being typical of

---

FIG. 25.—*Fossils from the Chalk.*

1. *Micraster leskei* (Desmoulins); 2. *Offaster pilula* (Lamarck); 3. *Micraster coranguinum* (Leske); 4. *Marsupites testudinarius* (Schlotheim); 5. *Uintacrinus westfalicus* Schlueter; 6. *Inoceramus labiatus* (Schlotheim) (× $\frac{2}{3}$); 7. *Holaster planus* (Mantell); 8, a, b. *Terebratulina lata* Etheridge (× 2); 9, a, b. *Orbirhynchia cuvieri* (d'Orbigny); 10. *Schloenbachia varians* (J. Sowerby); 11. *Actinocamax plenus* (Blainville); 12. *Holaster subglobosus* (Leske).

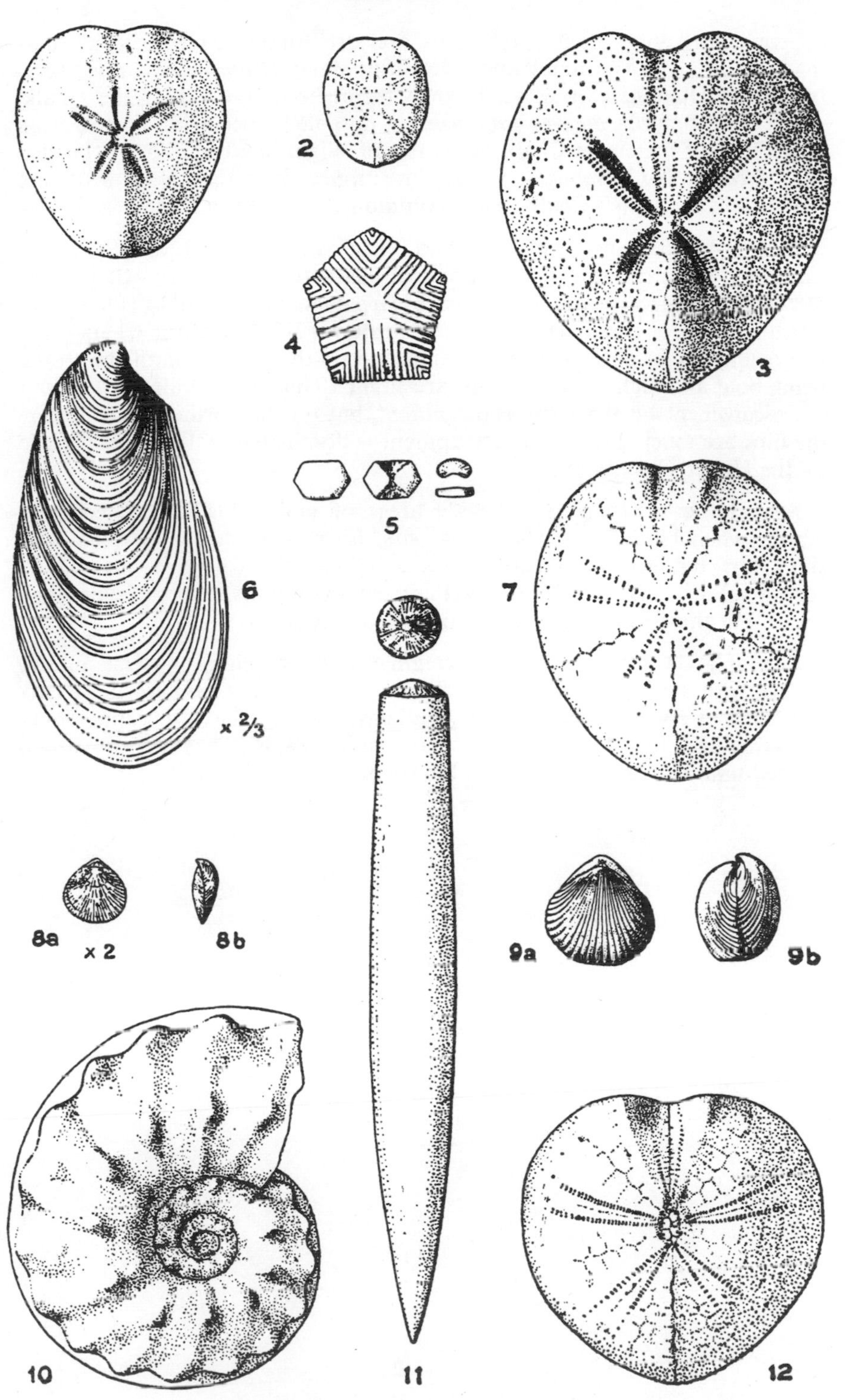

FIG. 25.—*Fossils from the Chalk*

different horizons. Brachiopod shells are also found at all horizons, particularly in the Cornstones and Chloritic Marl; *Cretirhynchia* and Terebratulid shells (*Gibbithyris*, etc.) range throughout the rest of the Chalk. Among the polyzoa *Bicavea rotaformis* is notable as occurring in profusion at the base of the Upper Chalk in the Isle of Wight in a bed (6 to 8 ft) called the ' *Bicavea* Bed.' Sponges, already mentioned from the lowest beds, are frequent in the Upper Chalk, being commonly enclosed in flint.

On account of its great thickness and fairly uniform constitution the Chalk formation gives rise to extensive areas of characteristic scenery—that of the Downland type, with the associated escarpments and coombes (Pl. VII A). Irregular lines of escarpments form the western boundary of the Chalk. The slopes and height of the escarpments depend on the inclination of the strata, being bold and high where the dips are slight. Thus in the Vale of Wardour the escarpment on the south is prominent, but on the northern side, where the dips are much greater, the escarpment is dominated by the ridge formed by the Upper Greensand.

Behind the escarpments are wide areas of undulating upland country, which, when bare of superficial deposits, form open downs covered with short turf but generally without trees. Where the Chalk is covered by superficial deposits such as brickearth or clay-with-flints, tracts of woodland occur, but these have been cleared over wide areas.

The uplands are dissected by irregular and branching systems of dry valleys with steeply sloping sides. Such valleys are dry because the Chalk is absorbent and rain soaks in very quickly, but they have the appearance of having been formed by running brooks and streams. They were obviously formed under conditons which no longer prevail.

A. CHESIL BANK FROM WEST CLIFF, PORTLAND

B. SCENERY TYPICAL OF BAGSHOT BEDS: NEAR WAREHAM, DORSET
(*For details see p.* iv)

IV. TERTIARY STRATA

EOCENE FORMATIONS

A CONSIDERABLE PART of the Hampshire Basin is occupied by Eocene strata. These strata are among the earliest deposits laid down during the Tertiary Era, and were so named because the fossils found in them have affinities with present-day forms of life (Greek, *eos*, dawn; *kainos*, recent).

The Eocene beds in the area rest always on the Chalk, with a conspicuous surface of demarcation between, and a long interval elapsed before these Eocene beds were laid down on the surface of the Chalk. During this time the whole area was raised as a land mass and was acted upon by the agents of denudation; it was also subjected to slight earth-movements which produced gentle tilting and folding. Subsequently when the early Eocene sea invaded the area the crests of these low folds were worn down, as is shown, for example, by the local variations in thickness of the uppermost zone of the Chalk in the Isle of Wight. The uplift near the area of the present Vale of Pewsey was much greater, for several hundred feet of chalk were removed, and the Eocene deposits rest on the Middle Chalk.

Meanwhile considerable geographic changes had taken place since the deposition of the Chalk, for the Eocene beds are mostly sands and clays, and present a marked contrast with the familar white limestone of the Chalk. Notable changes in the forms of life had also taken place; and the contrast between the fossils of the Eocene and the Chalk is as marked as the nature of the beds which contain them. With the end of the Secondary Era the great reptiles like the ichthyosaurs and the dinosaurs disappeared; the ammonites died out; true birds took the place of the flying reptiles. In the Tertiary Era mammals became the dominant vertebrates, while invertebrates such as the mollusca and corals became more akin to present-day forms.

The Eocene beds of the Hampshire Basin represent the western part of an extensive area of deposition known as the Anglo-Franco-Belgian Basin, an area of frequent changes in geographical conditions. These changes are reflected in the constitution and fossil content of the deposits; and long after these deposits were consolidated the whole area was affected by earth-movements and denudation. In England two regions of this large area now remain—the Hampshire Basin and the London Basin. Correlation of beds in different parts of the Basin is largely putative because of the frequent changes in facies, but as Dudley Stamp and later G. F. Elliott and A. G. Davis have made clear, the constitution and disposition of the strata fit in with the idea of a series of cycles of sedimentation. Each cycle began with an invasion of the sea, followed by shallow and deeper water; then came a reversal through shallow water to estuarine and finally continental conditions. Each phase produced different types of sedimentation, with which were associated the contemporary forms of life.

READING BEDS

The earliest deposits of the Eocene series in the Hampshire Basin are the Reading Beds, which take their name from the town around which they are well developed. These beds, the average thickness of which is about 103 ft., were deposited mostly under fluviatile conditions, but there are evidences of estuarine and lagoon conditions, and the estuary evidently opened out to the east, because towards Sussex the beds become more marine, while in the west, in Dorset, they appear as gravels.

In lithic character the Reading Beds are extremely variable, consisting of sand, loam, clay, bands of concretionary ironstone, beds of flint pebbles and gravel; occasionally seams of clay contain well-preserved leaves. The bulk of the formation consists of red mottled clays. Where the basement bed can be seen it rests on a much-eroded surface of the Chalk, and includes a layer of green-stained flints, with sandy loam above. In places a definite Bottom Bed is developed, evidently of marine origin, for it yields fish teeth and oyster shells (*Ostrea bellovacina*); this bed is usually a green sand and is of an average thickness of 10 feet (Fig. 26).

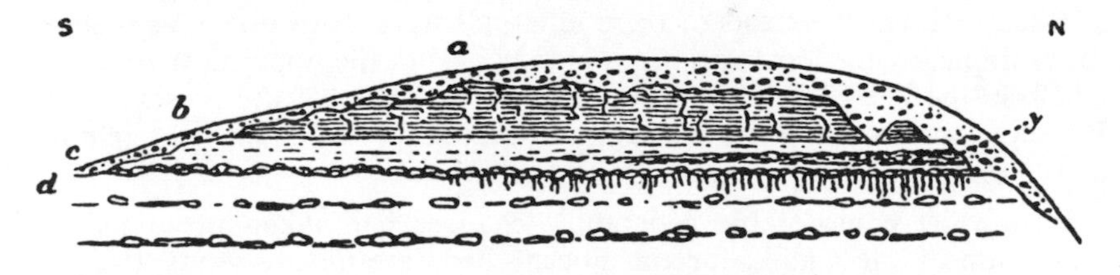

a. Gravel, *b.* Mottled clay, *c.* Bottom bed; greenish sand with (*y*) oyster-bed. *d.* Chalk.

FIG. 26.—*Section showing the junction of the Chalk and Reading Beds on the railway near Kembridge*

(After H. J. Osborne White, ' Geology of Winchester and Stockbridge ' (*Mem. Geol. Survey*), 1912, p. 51)

The outcrop of the Reading Beds extends as a narrow belt along the border of the Chalk, where that formation dips beneath the Tertiary strata. In the Isle of Wight, where the Chalk dips almost vertically, the outcrop is extremely narrow. At various localities the Reading Beds have been used for making bricks and pottery.

LONDON CLAY

After the deposition of the Reading Beds the area was submerged beneath the sea, for the succeeding London Clay contains fossils which show it to be entirely of marine origin. This formation consists of blue, brown and grey clay, yellow and grey sands and sandy loam, interspersed with pebble beds; it includes also local developments of sandstone. The London Clay of the Hampshire Basin was evidently deposited in shallow seas and presents a contrast to the more uniform and deeper water clays of the London Basin. As described by G. F. Elliott and A. G. Davis, the sea that laid down these deposits came from the area of the North Sea Basin and spread over the site of the London Basin before it invaded the Hampshire area. Here it merged with a branch of the southern sea (the Tethys) which brought a warm current and spread warm-water mollusca and other organisms over the area. Later the sea regressed eastwards.

The London Clay rests with a slightly eroded but sharp junction on the Reading Beds. At the base the beds are sandy, and generally with rounded flints, and in places the basement bed contains innumerable tubes of the marine worm *Ditrupa*. A shelly calcareous sandstone, the Bognor Rock, is developed at Portsmouth and Bognor. The London Clay varies in thickness. Of some 400 ft exposed in Alum Bay, the upper 170 ft are sandy and unfossiliferous and may equally well be grouped with the overlying Bagshot Beds. The formation is 300 ft thick in the east of the Isle of Wight, 70-80 ft in the Purbeck district and only a few feet in Wiltshire. It thins out westwards and is overstepped near Dorchester by the Bagshot Beds. In places it passes gradually upwards to the Bagshot Beds.

Fossils are irregularly distributed in the London Clay, but common at certain horizons; they are mostly molluscan shells, among them *Panopea intermedia*, *Pholadomya margaritacea*, and *Pinna affinis*. Some forms, *e.g. Glycymeris* and *Turritella* are abundant and form shell-beds in places; and many species of fossils are peculiar to the Hampshire Basin. Crabs (*Palaeocorystes glabra* and *Xanthopsis leachii*), lobsters (*Hoploparia*) and tubes of the marine worm *Rotularia* [*Vermicularia*] *bognoriensis* are found, but vertebrate remains (common in parts of the London Basin) are rare. Plant-remains are also rare in the area, but fruits of the tropical palm *Nipa* (of which a modern form is found in the coastal and estuarine swamps of Indonesia and Malaya) have been found at Portsmouth.

The outcrop of the London Clay runs as a belt parallel to that formed by the Reading Beds, and about twice its width; and the land formed by this division is wet and heavy. Until comparatively recent times most of the surface area of the London Clay was covered by oak forests; about a quarter of it is still woodland.

BAGSHOT BEDS

The name Bagshot Beds was first given to beds of sand with seams of pebbles and beds of white and grey clay, which succeed the London Clay in the London Basin. The beds vary from place to place, and correlation is largely conjectural. In the Hampshire Basin the term Bagshot Beds has been applied to various sandy strata resting on the London Clay, and varying in thickness from about 30 ft near Portsmouth to 772 ft at Alum Bay. Nowadays, however, the name is restricted to the lowest part of the beds at Alum Bay and to various locally named divisions (such as Bournemouth Freshwater Beds, Studland Series, Redend Sandstone, Pipeclay Series and Agglestone Grit) on the mainland. The Bournemouth Marine Beds and the Lower Bracklesham Beds have been correlated with the Middle division, and the Upper Bracklesham Beds with the Upper division of the Bagshot Beds in the wide sense.

In Hampshire and the Isle of Wight the Bagshot Beds consist of bright yellow and white sands with impersistent seams of pipe-clay which have yielded leaves of fig-trees, laurels, aralias, and other sub-tropical plants, and fragments of fan-palm. The series is variable in thickness, being 138 ft in the east of the Isle of Wight and 76 ft in the west; the beds thin rapidly northwards and eastwards. When traced westwards into Dorset, they show marked changes, becoming coarser and gravelly, and overlap on to lower beds. Thus at Warmwell they cut through the London Clay and rest on the Reading Beds.

In the Bournemouth area the passage from the London Clay to the Bagshot Beds shows loams of the London Clay passing up into the coarse current-bedded sands with intercalated pipe-clays and subordinate loams that comprise 200-250 ft of Bagshot Beds. Here two divisions are recognized: a Lower or Pipe-clay division and an Upper division known as the Bournemouth Freshwater Beds. These are evidently deltaic deposits, probably of

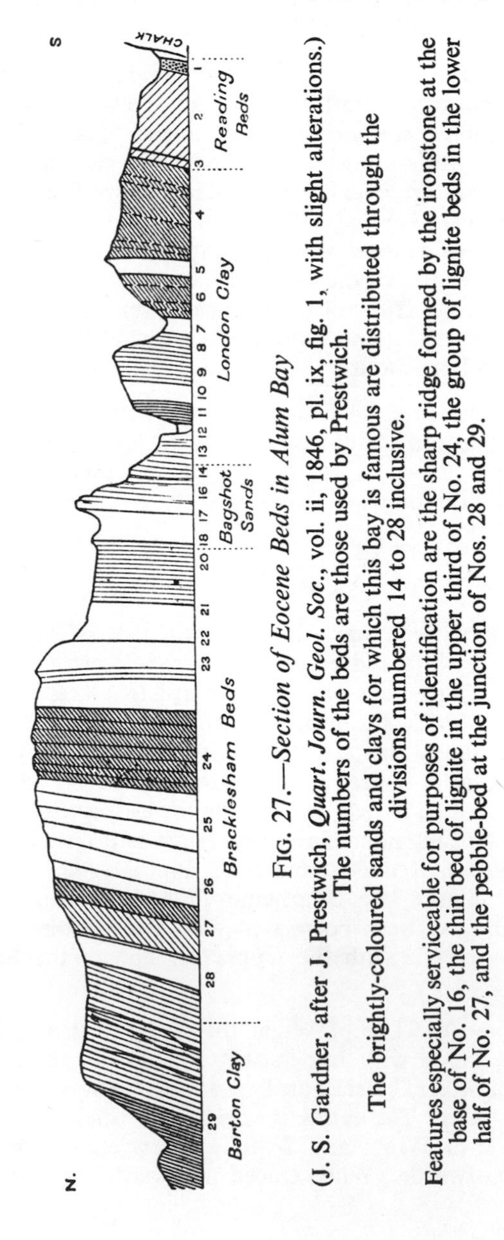

FIG. 27.—*Section of Eocene Beds in Alum Bay*

(J. S. Gardner, after J. Prestwich, *Quart. Journ. Geol. Soc.*, vol. ii, 1846, pl. ix, fig. 1, with slight alterations.) The numbers of the beds are those used by Prestwich.

The brightly-coloured sands and clays for which this bay is famous are distributed through the divisions numbered 14 to 28 inclusive.

Features especially serviceable for purposes of identification are the sharp ridge formed by the ironstone at the base of No. 16, the thin bed of lignite in the upper third of No. 24, the group of lignite beds in the lower half of No. 27, and the pebble-bed at the junction of Nos. 28 and 29.

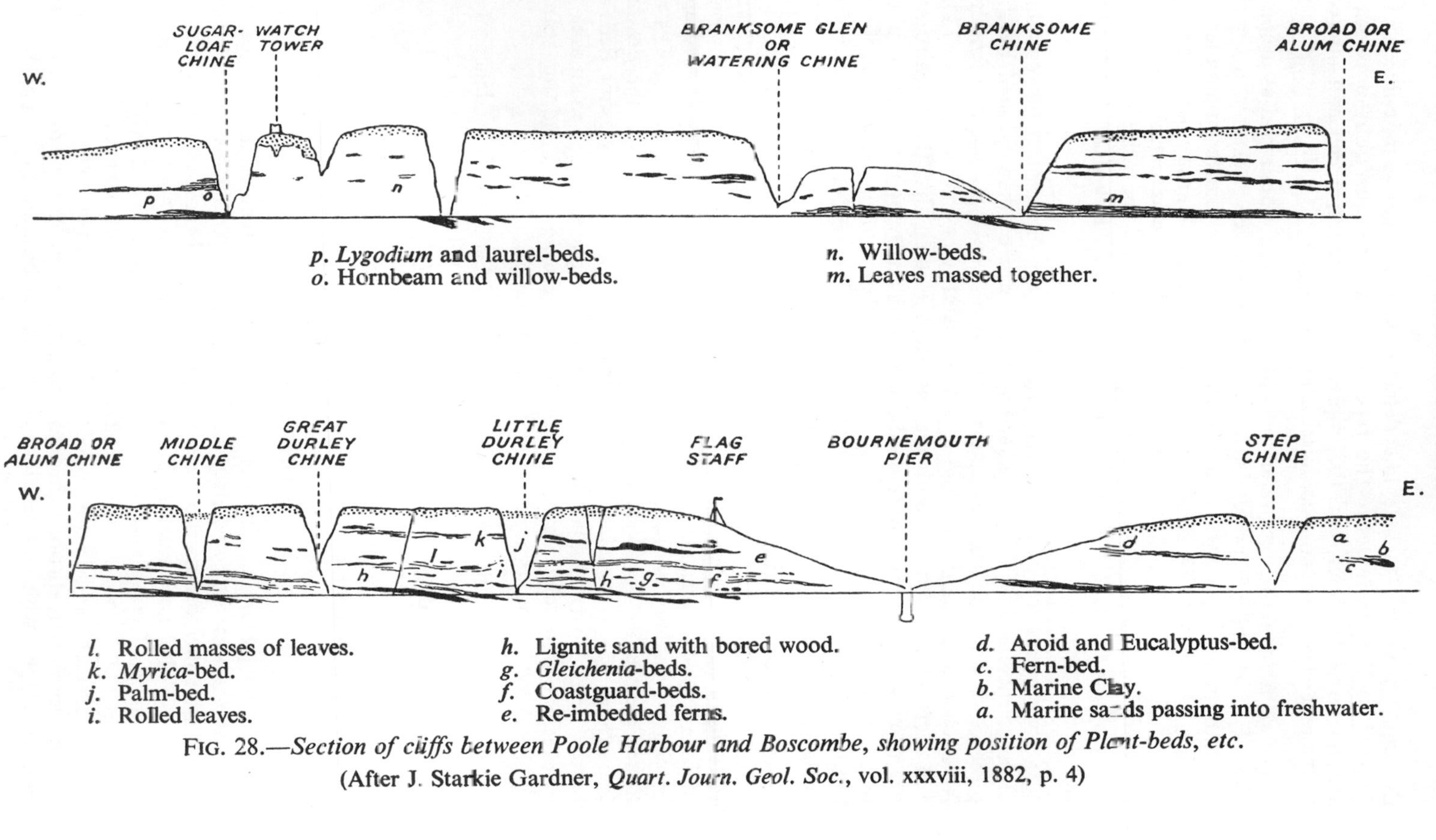

FIG. 28.—*Section of cliffs between Poole Harbour and Boscombe, showing position of Plant-beds, etc.*
(After J. Starkie Gardner, *Quart. Journ. Geol. Soc.*, vol. xxxviii, 1882, p. 4)

the same river, and include fine detritus derived from granite-like rocks situated to the south-west. The pipe-clay beds are most fully developed around Poole Harbour, and the impressions of leaves, which add interest to the pipe-clays, are more common near Studland and Corfe.

The Bournemouth Freshwater Beds have been aptly described as a complex of white and yellow sands, laminated carbonaceous clays and loams and thin impure pipe-clays, arranged for the most part in overlapping lenses of all sizes up to a few hundred yards in diameter. Plant-remains, chiefly leaves, are again found in these pipe-clays, and are representative of forest trees, conifers, ferns, palms and marsh vegetation. The principal section of these upper beds is exposed in the cliffs between Poole Head and the lift east of Bournemouth Pier (Fig. 28).

In their westward extension the gravels of the Bagshot Beds resemble those of the Reading Beds in coarseness, but can be distinguished by the presence of white quartz, subangular Palaeozoic rocks, fragments of radiolarian chert and schorl rock and a certain quantity of Purbeck rocks. Flint and chert are common to both gravels. It is evident that the constituents of the gravels were brought from the west, principally by river action; also, that not only was the Chalk deeply eroded before and during Eocene times but that the Upper Greensand, Purbeck and perhaps older rocks were being denuded at no great distance westwards.

Several outliers of Bagshot Beds occur on the downs west of the Tertiary basin, the most important being those on Bincombe Down and Blackdown. Here again they are overlapping and rest directly on the Chalk; they consist of interbedded gravel, clay and sand. Much of the sand and gravel of the Blackdown outlier has been cemented into a conglomerate, and blocks of these 'greywethers' or 'sarsen-stones' are left scattered over the downs. (*see also* p. 93) Over most of the outcrop the land of the Bagshot Beds is barren heath, sparsely inhabited (Pl. VIII B). In places in the main area it gives rise to waterlogged sandy heaths, both ironstone 'pan' and thin seams of clay throwing out ground-water at various levels.

Locally, as near Bournemouth, the Bagshot Beds afford evidence of a sinking of the area which allowed the sea to encroach and thus begin the next phase of marine deposition. Signs of the impending encroachment were noticed in the upper members of the Freshwater Series, where J. Starkie Gardner observed interdigitation between these beds and those of the Bournemouth Marine Beds.

BRACKLESHAM BEDS

The Bracklesham Beds were so named from strata exposed in Bracklesham Bay, on the west side of Selsey peninsula. Later, certain beds in the New Forest were included as the upper members of the Bracklesham succession, because of the close relationship of their fossils to those of the beds at Bracklesham. The full succession is in Whitecliff Bay, Isle of Wight, and this was chosen by Osmond Fisher (1862) as the type-section, where he recognized 4 main divisions and 19 subdivisions. Two broad divisions have long been in use—the lower, distinguished by the presence of *Nummulites laevigatus*, and the Upper, with *Nummulites variolarius*, the base of the Upper division being marked by a change in the fauna, and by water-worn shells and pebbles. The discovery by A. Wrigley and A. G. Davis (1937) of *Nummulites planulatus* in Fisher's Bed IV of the Lower division, however, shows that there are three divisions, as distinguished by the limited range of the nummulites. This is congruous with the constitution of two of the subdivisions, Bed V and Bed VIII, which show non-marine features. Both beds include root-clays or 'underclays,' indicating that plant-life flourished on the spot, presumably in swamps near sea-level. Bed V overlies the bed with *Nummulites planulatus*; in the upper part of Bed VIII are clays and lignitic seams that overlie the last band with *Nummulites laevigatus*,

The Bracklesham Beds show considerable lateral variation and in general there is a lateral passage from marine conditions in the east to freshwater in the west. At Bracklesham the beds are wholly marine, although at Bournemouth the greater part is fluvio-marine and freshwater. At Alum Bay nearly the whole is estuarine and lignitic, except for 36 ft of shell-beds at the top. In thickness they are 200 ft at Bramble Hill, near Bramshaw, 300 ft at Netley, near Southampton, and 600 ft in the Isle of Wight. Most of the beds are clays, clayey sands or sands, with occasional bands of lignite and pebble-beds. Beds of sandy limestone form rocks, made up of *Alveolina* and other foraminifera, south of Selsey Bill.

The Bracklesham Beds have yielded an abundant fauna of tropical or sub-tropical aspect. Among the fossils which indicate these conditions are remains of crocodiles and sea-snakes, shells of large volutes, cowries, cones, mitres and nautili. Altogether more than 500 species of molluscan shells have been found. Fossils are so common in places that beds have been named after them, *e.g.* the *Cardita* Bed (with *Cardita* (*Venericor*) *planicosta*), the *Turritella* Bed (with *Turritella spp.*) and the Palate Bed, with remains of fish. *Corbula pisum*, *Amusium corneum*, *Macrosolen hollowaysi* and *Turritella* (*Ispharina*) *sulcifera* are among the common shells. Several beds are crowded with *Nummulites*.

The fluvio-marine and freshwater beds that are well developed near Bournemouth are partly of Bracklesham, partly of Barton age. The 'Bournemouth Marine Beds' (about 50 ft) are grey and yellow sands and dark laminated clays, with much lignite. Although styled marine (to distinguish them from the earlier freshwater beds) there are but few traces of marine episodes. They are mostly fluvio-marine, presenting the seaward facies of a deltaic formation, and are possibly of Upper Bracklesham age. In some places the beds contain seeds, fruits and leaves of plants, among them the palm *Nipa*, and *Dryandra*. The 'Boscombe Sands,' which follow, are of littoral origin and consist of white and yellow current-bedded sands, with some lignite and shingle. They have yielded no fossils, but the shingle banks may attenuate eastwards into the basal pebble-bed of the Barton Beds. Next are the 'Hengistbury Beds,' which were laid down in deeper water and have yielded marine fossils, such as *Protocardia*, *Corbula* and *Crassatella*; Mr. Curry has recorded *Nummulites prestwichianus* in the lower olive-green sandy clays with pebbles, thus establishing a correlation with the Lower Barton Beds. Above are laminated silty clays, chocolate-brown in colour. Courses of large 'doggers' of red-brown ironstone are a conspicuous feature of these beds.

BARTON BEDS

The Barton Beds take their name from the locality on the Hampshire coast, in Christchurch Bay. Here they pass upwards from the Bracklesham Beds and extend continuously from Cliff End, ¾ mile E. of Mudeford to Long Mead End. The beds vary in lithology and palaeontological changes are observable in the sequence. In constitution the beds are mostly sands and clays of predominantly marine origin; bands of concretionary limestone are conspicuous near the middle of the succession. A few of the beds yield only a small number of fossils, but several are highly fossiliferous; more than 500 species have been recorded. The most common fossils are molluscan shells. Corals are rare, except *Turbinolia* and *Graphularia*. Cirripedes and crabs are also rare. Bryozoa are fairly common and 18 species are recorded. Teeth of the fish *Synodontaspis* are frequently found, and about 40 species of otoliths are recorded.

For the purposes of Geological Survey mapping two main divisions have been used—Barton Clay and Barton Sands. On the basis of the distribution of fossils three major divisions were first established; later, more detailed work by Mr. E. St. John Burton showed that 13 subdivisions (denoted by the letters cited in the following account) can be recognized; but for general purposes a tripartite division (Lower, Middle and Upper) will suffice.

The Lower Barton Beds yield two species of *Nummulites* that are important as horizon-markers. *Nummulites prestwichianus* (=*elegans*) occurs in a thin bed (A1) that has been taken as the base of the Barton Beds, but Mr. D. Curry has chosen as a datum the pebble-bed 10 ft lower, because it marks a natural break in the succession. *Nummulites rectus* has been described by Mr. Curry as marking an horizon (A2) 20 ft above the bed with *Nummulites prestwichianus*. The clays above this horizon (A2) include shelly drifts, with *Turricula*, *Athleta* &c. Higher up are the Highcliffe Sands (A3), with rare patches of shells. At the top of the Lower Barton Beds is a layer (B, 4 ft) with *Pholadomya*.

The Middle Barton Beds (C-F, 51 ft) are mostly clays. This is the best division for well-preserved shells, the most spectacular coming from the 5 ft Earthy Bed (E), just above the middle. *Athleta luctator* and species of *Clavilithes* are conspicuous among the large number of common shells.

The Upper Barton Beds (95 ft) begin with the Stone Band (G, 1 ft), an indurated mass of shell-fragments. Above this is the *Chama* Bed (H, 18 ft), a blue-grey clay with shells of *Chama squamosa* in conspicuous abundance. Next in succession, after 26 ft of unfossiliferous sands (I), are the grey-brown clays of the Becton Bunny Bed (J, 26 ft). These clays contain fragile shells of estuarine as well as marine genera, and are succeeded by the pale sands of the Long Mead End Bed (K, 20 ft). Near the top of this bed shells are found massed together; they include *Polymesoda* [*Cyrena*] *convexa*, *Batillaria concava* and *Bayania fasciata*. At the top of the Upper Barton Beds is a layer (L, 4 ft) of dark clays with crushed shells. The fossils of the higher beds of the Upper Barton indicate brackish conditions.

OLIGOCENE FORMATIONS

The Oligocene Period, like the Eocene Period which it followed, was so named from the relationship of its forms of life to those of the present day (Greek, *oligos*, few; *kainos*, recent). The Eocene marked the dawn of modern life: the Oligocene shows a slight increase in the proportion of modern elements. At the beginning of the Oligocene Period, geographic conditions in the Hampshire Basin were a continuation of those prevailing at the end of Eocene times; but upward movement of the land gave rise to an area of lagoons and freshwater lakes, opening into estuaries and arms of the contracting sea. Occasionally the sea encroached over the area. A varied series of deposits was the natural product of these unstable conditions. Fossils are abundant throughout the series, shells occurring in profusion. Certain beds have yielded plant-remains, including leaves of palms and water-lilies; and remains of crocodiles, turtles, mammals and fish are commonly found.

The Oligocene beds occupy the northern half of the Isle of Wight and the southern part of the New Forest on the mainland opposite. They are well exposed in the coast sections on the Isle of Wight and on the Hampshire coast at Hordle. An interesting outlier forms the isolated hill of Creech-barrow, between Corfe and Lulworth, in Dorset. The four divisions recognized—the Headon, Osborne, Bembridge and Hamstead Beds—are named after localities in the Isle of Wight where they are well developed. This series of beds comprises the whole of the 'Fluvio-Marine Beds,' first described by Thomas Webster in 1816, and further studied by Edward Forbes in 1853. Modern Continental classification would probably place the base of the Oligocene below the Middle Headon Beds, and include the Lower Headon Beds in the Eocene.

HEADON BEDS

These beds, which in the Isle of Wight, are 147 ft in thickness at Headon Hill and 212 ft in Whitecliff Bay, include coloured clays, with occasional sandbeds, some lignite and bands of limestone. Three stages (Lower, Middle and Upper) are recognized in this division. Fossils, mostly shells, are abundant throughout. In the freshwater beds gastropods are particularly common, and include *Galba* [*Limnaea*] *longiscata*, *Planorbina euomphalus* and *Viviparus lentus*. *Stenothyra* [*Nematura*] *parvula* indicates brackish water. The commonest lamellibranchs of the freshwater and brackish beds are species of *Erodona* and *Corbicula* [*Cyrena*]. The typical marine shells include *Nucula headonensis*, *Ostrea vectensis*, and *Globularia harrisi*. Gastropods common in the marine and estuarine beds are *Batillaria concava*, *Melanopsis morrisi*, *Pollia labiata*, *Ancilla buccinoides*, *Theodoxus apertus* and *T. concavus*.

FIG. 29.—*Fossils from the Eocene Beds.*

1. *Turritella* (*Ispharina*) *sulcifera* Deshayes (× $\frac{1}{2}$); 2. *Clavilithes macrospira* Cossmann (× $\frac{2}{3}$); 3. *Sycostoma pyrus* (Solander) (× $\frac{2}{3}$); 4. *Fusinus porrectus* (Solander); 5. *Calliostoma nodulosum* (Solander); 6. *Rimella rimosa* (Solander); 7, a, b. *Volutocorbis ambigua* (Solander) (× $\frac{2}{3}$); 8. *Olivella branderi* (J. Sowerby); 9. *Typhis pungens* (Solander); 10. *Crassatella sulcata* (Solander); 11. *Xanthopsis leachii* (Desmarest) (under surface × $\frac{1}{2}$); 12. *Cardita* (*Venericor*) *planicosta* (Lamarck) (× $\frac{1}{2}$); 13. *Calyptraea aperta* (Solander); 14. *Glycymeris deletus* (Solander); 15. *Chama squamosa* Solander; 16. *Panopea intermedia* J. Sowerby.

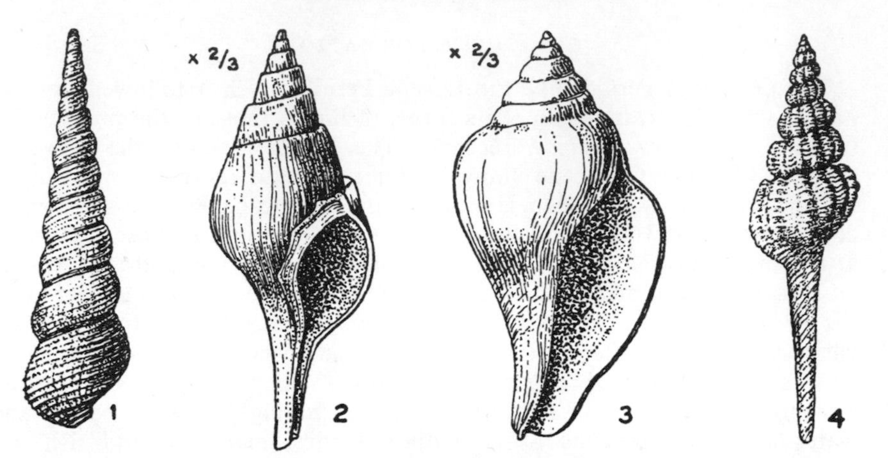

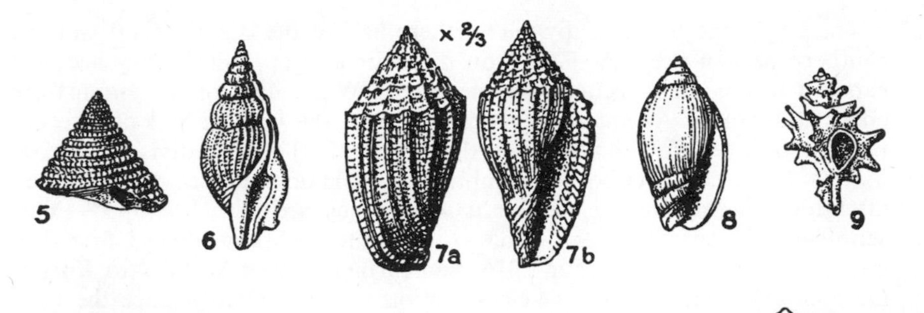

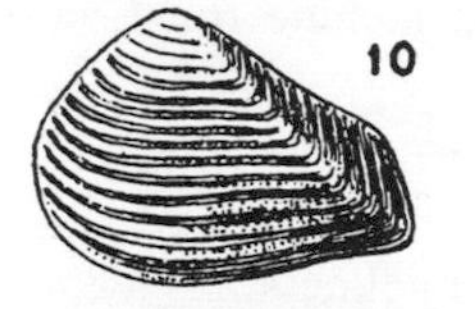

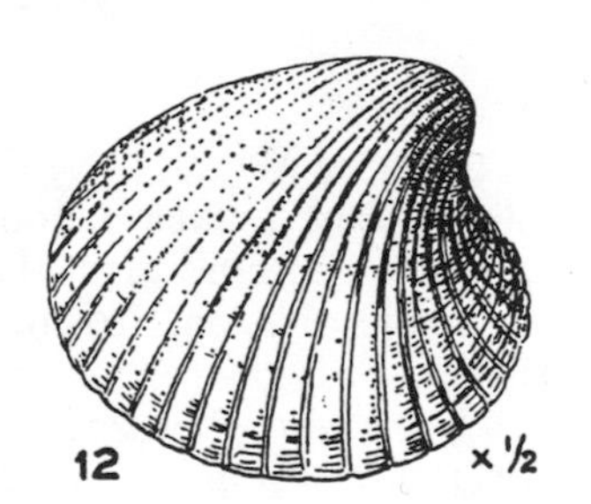

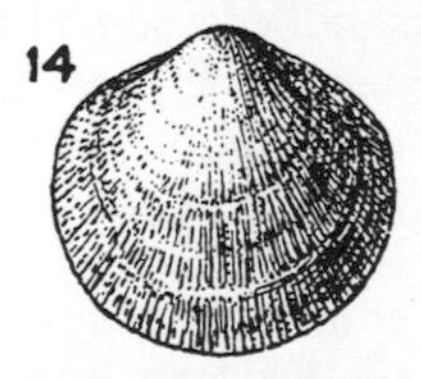

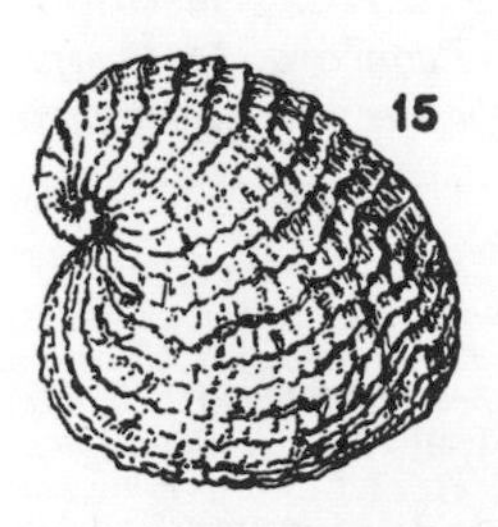

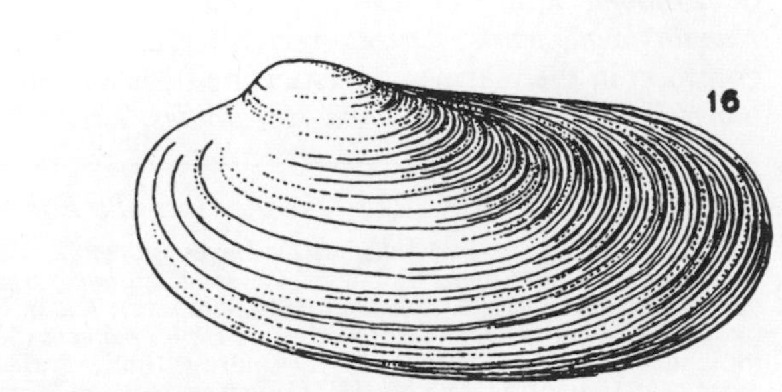

FIG. 29.—*Fossils from the Eocene Beds*
For explanation see footnote p. 69

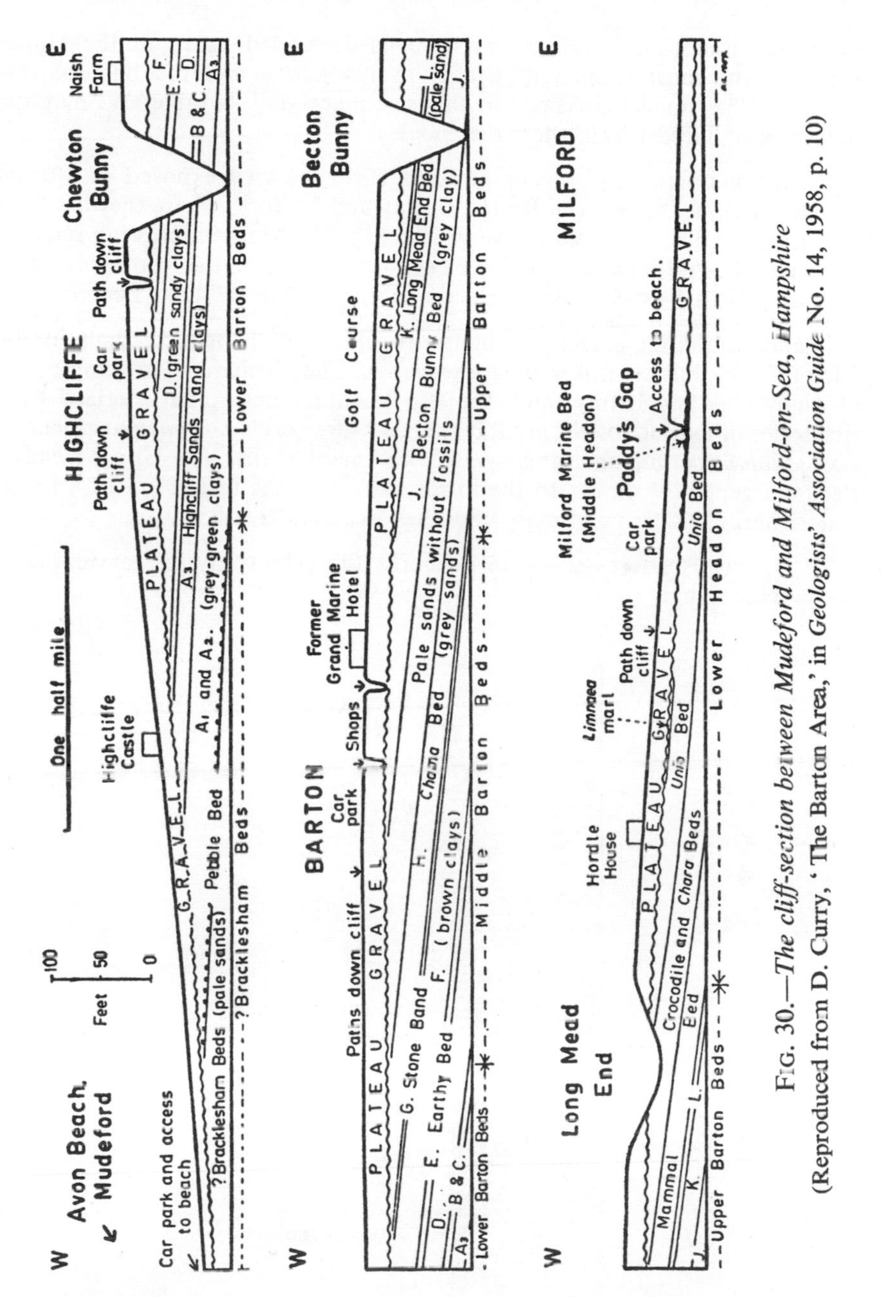

FIG. 30.—*The cliff-section between Mudeford and Milford-on-Sea, Hampshire*
(Reproduced from D. Curry, 'The Barton Area,' in *Geologists' Association Guide* No. 14, 1958, p. 10)

Certain distinctive beds in the Headon series of Headon Hill may be noted. At the top of the Lower Headon Beds (61 ft) is a bed of cream-coloured Limnaean limestone, the How Ledge Limestone, largely composed of the freshwater gastropod *Galba*. In the middle of the overlying Middle Headon (33 ft) is the '*Venus* Bed' (6 to 15 ft), named after the common occurrence of the bivalved shell *Sinodia* (*Cordiopsis*) *suborbicularis*, first included in the genus *Venus*. In the upper part of the Middle Headon are two thin beds of

Limnaean limestone. Similar limestone is developed again in the Upper Headon; the most prominent bed is that which marks the base of this division. The smaller divisions in this series are very variable and may die out or be replaced within short distances.

On the mainland the Lower Headon Beds are well exposed in Hordle (or Hordwell) Cliff, between Becton Bunny and Milford, where they are 82 ft in thickness. The succession is shown in Fig. 31. Many interesting remains of mammals, reptiles and birds have been obtained from the Mammalia Bed, and more than 50 species of plants are represented in the Leaf Bed.

Inland, the Middle Headon Beds are more purely marine than in the Isle of Wight, but are not well exposed now. They include alternating bands of sandy clay and loamy sand, the Brockenhurst Beds, characterized by a rich series of marine fossils, notably the very rare corals *Solenastrea granulata Lobopsammia cariosa* and other species, and many shells. The Upper Headon Beds are generally similar to the lower beds, and the fossils are of a fresh-water character: the main mass underlies Beaulieu Heath.

The Lower Headon Beds were formerly dug extensively for marling land and brickmaking.

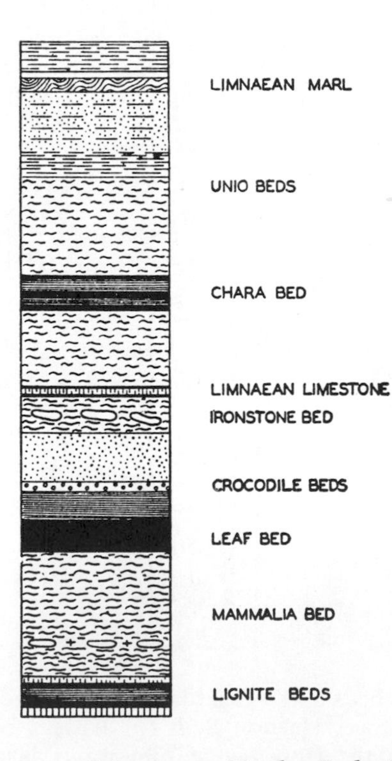

FIG. 31.—*Section of the Lower Headon Beds, Hordle Cliff*

Scale, about 1 in. = 24 ft.

(Adapted from Gardner, Keeping and Monckton, *Quart. Journ. Geol. Soc.*, vol. xliv, 1888, p. 596)

OSBORNE BEDS

Except for a small outlier on the mainland, near Lyndhurst, these beds are restricted to the Isle of Wight, where they are 80 ft in thickness on the west and east, and 110 ft in the north. They consist of brackish and fresh-water clays and marls, some highly coloured, occasional hard bands and bands of concretionary limestone. Shells (*Galba*, *Viviparus*, etc.) of the same species as those in the Headon Beds, are of common occurrence, and in places beds of limestone are full of them. Nucules of the lime-secreting aquatic plant *Chara* are plentiful in the limestones. Remains of fish (*Amia*, *Diplomystus*), reptiles (*Alligator*, *Emys* and *Trionyx*), prawns (*Propalaemon*) and mammals (*Palaeotherium* and *Theridomys*) are also found in other beds. A thin bed of clay with abundant specimens of *Diplomystus* [*Clupea*] *vectensis* is exposed on the shore west of the mouth of Wootton Creek. On the north-eastern shores of the island the Osborne Beds are represented by an upper sandy series (St. Helens Sands) and a lower series of coarse indurated beds (Nettlestone Grits).

BEMBRIDGE BEDS

These comprise two divisions, the Bembridge Limestone below and the Bembridge Marls above. The Limestone is 18 ft in thickness in the west of the Isle of Wight and 22 ft in the east, but well-records indicate that it is much thinner in the concealed area, particularly near Ryde. It consists of massive beds of freshwater limestone with intercalated greenish clays and marls. On account of its persistence, its outcrop is easily recognized; it can be conveniently studied in Whitecliff Bay, but is not so well exposed on Headon Hill. Among the fossils are the freshwater gastropods of the Headon Beds and the large land-shells *Filholia elliptica* and *Megalocochlea globosa*. Mammalian remains include those of *Palaeotherium*, *Hyopotamus* and *Anoplotherium*. The tiny nucules of *Chara* are also frequent in the limestone.

The only occurrence outside the Isle of Wight is the outlier at Creech-barrow, 2½ miles W. of Corfe Castle, Dorset, where it was identified by the presence of *Filholia elliptica*, *Palaeoxestina* [*Helix*] *occlusa* and a tooth of *Palaeotherium* among other fossils.

The Bembridge Marls are 70 ft in thickness in the west of the Isle of Wight and 120 ft in the east. They were deposited in a deltaic area with extensive mud flats, and consist of shelly brackish and freshwater clays and marls. At the base is a marine bed or beds with such fossils as the shells *Ostrea vectensis*, *Sinodia* (*Cordiopsis*) *suborbicularis* and *Sphenia minor*. Near the base also, in Thorness and Gurnard bays, is a layer of flat, discontinuous lenticles of fine-grained, blue hearted calcareous mudstone in which insect-remains, occasional leaves and freshwater shells occur in pockets. This layer is known as the Insect Bed; and twenty genera of insects, belonging to eight orders, have been identified. The majority of the interesting assemblage of plant-remains from the Bembridge Beds came from the Insect Bed. The plants represent a mixed flora, including conifers and other forest trees such as oak and beech, as well as ferns and horse-tails; and a warm-temperate and sub-tropical climate is indicated.

The succeeding beds in the series comprise grey or green clays and marls, rich in shells, the commonest being species of *Corbicula* and *Melanopsis*,

Melanoides acutus and *Viviparus lentus*. Land-shells are found occasionally. The small gastropod *Potamaclis turritissima* occurs in profusion in the highest beds, and near the top is a band crowded with the tiny gastropod *Nystia duchasteli*. The most complete section of the Marls is to be seen along the shore at Hamstead; there are also exposures in Thorness and Gurnard bays, in the cliff of Priory Bay, at St. Helens and in Whitecliff Bay.

HAMSTEAD BEDS

At the type-section in the cliffs between Hamstead and Bouldnor, in the Isle of Wight, these beds, which pass upwards gradually from the Bembridge Marls, are 255 ft in thickness. They include coloured clays, loams, sands and shales, mostly of freshwater origin, but with a marine phase in the uppermost beds. Two beds at the top of the marine clays contain shells that are broken and waterworn, bored by *Lithodomus* or overgrown by *Balanus*.

The following is a generalized sequence:—

	Ft
Marine clays (' *Corbula* Beds ') with *Corbula subpisum, Pirenella monilifera, Ostrea callifera, Athleta* (*Neoathleta*) *rathieri*, etc.	19½
Upper estuarine and freshwater beds (' *Cerithium* Beds ') with *Pirenella monilifera, Nystia duchasteli, Viviparus lentus, Unio, Corbicula*, etc.	11¾
Middle estuarine and freshwater beds, with *Bayania fasciata, Viviparus, Planorbis, Unio, Nystia* etc., and carbonaceous seams with plant-remains. ' White Band ' (clays and marls with shells) at the base	158¾
Lower estuarine and freshwater beds, with *Melanoides acutus, Stenothyra* [*Nematura*] *pupa, Galba, Planorbis, Sphenia minor, Polymesoda convexa* etc. The ' Black Band,' full of *Viviparus lentus* and *Unio*, at the base	65¾

In addition to shells, ostracods and plant-remains the Lower Hamstead Beds have yielded vertebrate fossils including *Anthracotherium, Ancodon*, and *Elotherium*.

The uppermost of the Hamstead Beds is the newest of the regular Tertiary deposits preserved in our area. Possibly other beds of the Oligocene series were laid down, but no trace now remains and the next stage in the history of this region is one of uplift, crustal movements and denudation.

FIG. 32.—*Fossils from the Oligocene Beds.*

1. *Potamides mutabilis* (Morris); 2. *Galba longiscata* (Brongniart); 3. *Athleta* (*Neoathleta*) *rathieri* (Hébert) (× 2); 4. *Pirenella monilifera* (Deshayes); 5. *Batillaria concava* (J. Sowerby); 6. *Viviparus lentus* (Solander); 7. *Nystia duchasteli* (Nyst) (× 5); 8. *Filholia elliptica* (J. Sowerby); 9. *Planorbina euomphalus* (J. Sowerby); 10. *Megalocochlea globosa* (J. Sowerby) (× ½); 11. *Melanopsis* sp.; 12. *Stenothyra* [*Nematura*] *parvula* (Morris) (× 5); 13. *Potamaclis turritissima* (Forbes) (× 3); 14. Nucule of *Chara tuberculata* Lyell (× 12); 15. *Erodona plana* (J. Sowerby); 16. *Corbula pisum* J. Sowerby (× 3); 17. *Corbicula obovata* (J. Sowerby); 18. *Nucula headonensis* Forbes; 19. *Polymesoda convexa* (Brongniart); 20. *Sphenia minor* (Morris); 21. *Sinodia* (*Cordiopsis*) *suborbicularis* (Goldfuss); 22. *Ostrea vectensis* Morris.

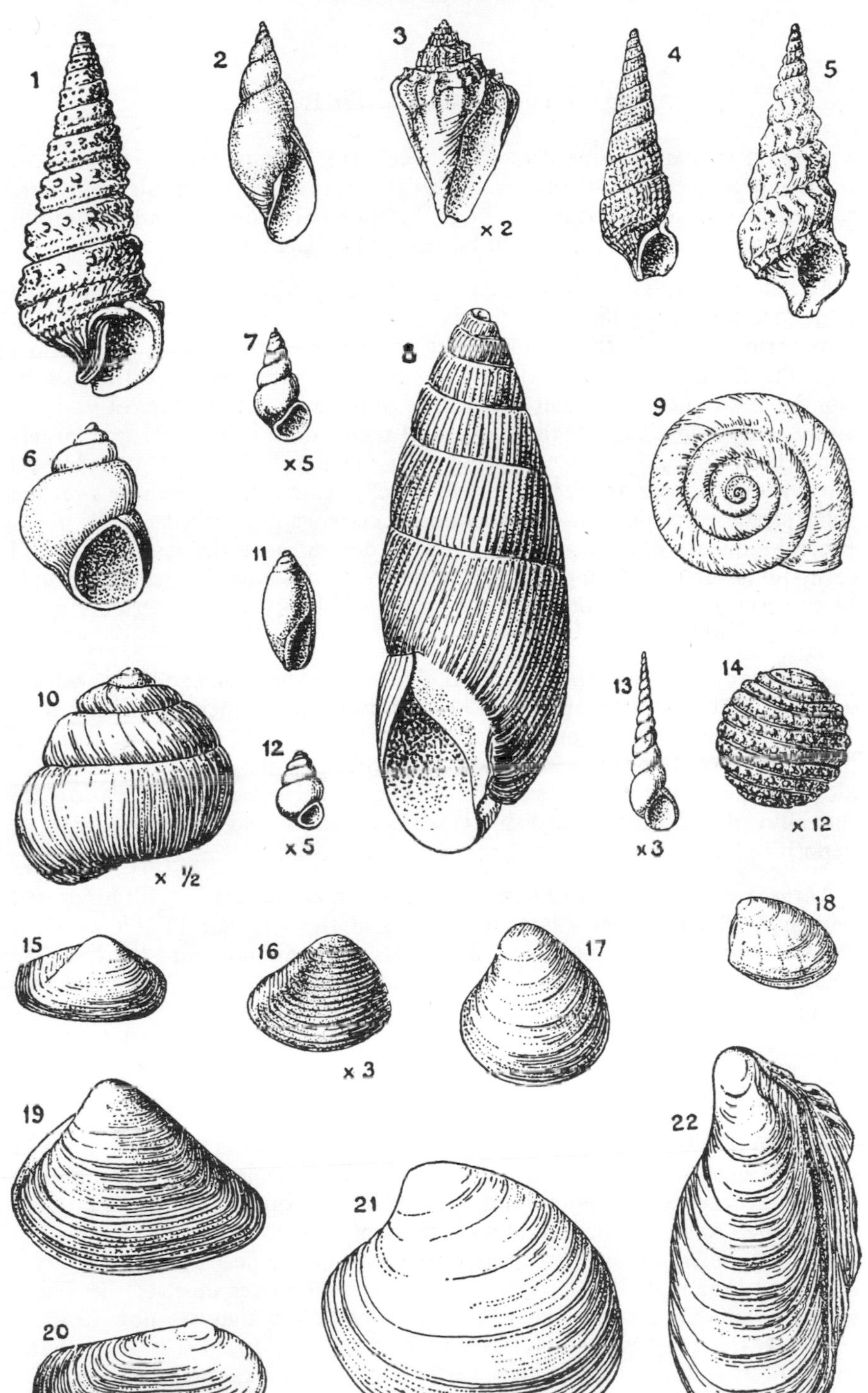

FIG. 32.—*Fossils from the Oligocene Beds*

V. SUPERFICIAL DEPOSITS

A LONG INTERVAL of time elapsed between the laying down of the last of the Oligocene beds and the formation of the next series of deposits that were formed in our area. During this interval important structural and geographical changes took place; these will be referred to later (p. 81).

The strata that have already been described, *i.e.* the Lias to the Hamstead Beds, are known as the Solid formations, and Superficial deposits, which were formed much later, are sometimes known as Drift deposits. In contrast with the Solid formations, which are of considerable geological age, substantial thickness and regular extent, the Superficial deposits are of variable and usually inconsiderable thickness, and their extent is irregular and largely dependent on topography. Representing the latest chapters in geological history, they appear as the ragged and patchy remnants of a mantle over the solid strata beneath. On this account a classification based strictly on a general sequence of events is not so readily devised as in the case of the solid formations. It will be appropriate therefore to describe the principal kinds of Superficial deposits before discussing the history of the period during which they were formed.

A large proportion of the Superficial deposits are gravels, and their position with regard to sea-level affords some help in deciding their respective ages. Thus one series occurs on plateaux near watersheds: these were formed before the present valleys were excavated. Others are arranged as terraces along the sides and lower parts of the valleys. Of much later formation are the alluvial deposits formed by existing streams and still in course of deposition.

Large areas of Superficial deposits, however, do not fit in with a gradual sequence. Such are the Clay-with-flints and the Angular Flint Gravel of the Downs; for these have been in process of formation since the time the Chalk was first acted upon by sub-aerial erosion; indeed, they are still being formed.

CLAY-WITH-FLINTS

Scattered over the high ground of the Chalk in patches and over areas of larger extent are accumulations of reddish or chocolate-coloured clay, in which are unworn flints, rounded pebbles and quantities of sand from Eocene deposits. Part of this is the product of long-continued decomposition of the Chalk *in situ* and part was derived from the destruction of Eocene deposits. Doubtless the deposit formerly extended over most of the Chalk surface, but this has since been dissected by valleys that are now dry. In thickness the Clay-with-flints varies from a few feet to 30 ft or more; and the deposit rests on an irregular surface of the Chalk, some of it in deep hollows or in cylindrical ' pipes ' (Fig. 33). In West Dorset a deposit similar in construction and origin is associated with the shattered chert beds of the Upper Greensand.

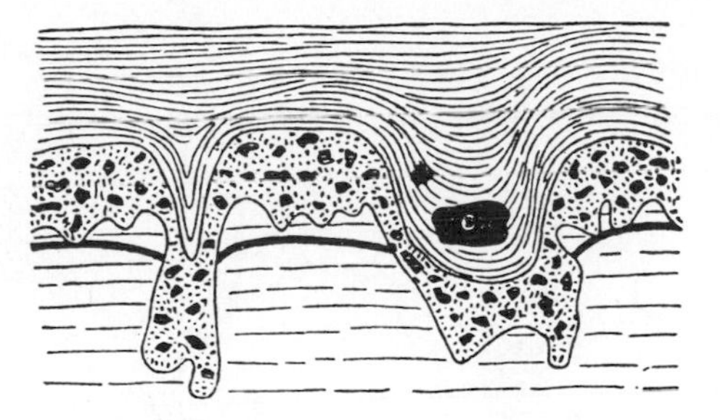

c. Sandstone [sarsen] embedded in the brick earth.

FIG. 33.—*Section of Clay-with-flints, near Wernham Farm, Overton Heath, Wiltshire*

(After T. Codrington, *Wilts. Arch. and Nat. Hist. Soc.*, vol. ix, no. 26, fig. 6)

ANGULAR FLINT GRAVEL OF THE DOWNS

On the higher parts of the Chalk Downs in the Isle of Wight and in South Dorset is a deposit similar in mode of occurrence and origin to the Clay-with-flints. It is a structureless gravel consisting of an accumulation of unworn and sometimes fragmentary flints in a matrix of quartz-sand, gritty powder or chalk-rubble. Occasionally rounded flint-pebbles from the Eocene deposits are included; or the presence of a reddish clay matrix shows its resemblance to the Clay-with-flints.

RAISED BEACHES

These are referred to (p. 83) in connexion with changes in sea-level during Pleistocene times. The highest is on the southern slope of Portsdown, east of Fareham, where an accumulation of shingle and sand lies banked against the Chalk at a level of about 100 ft O.D. The shingle is composed of rolled and imperfectly rounded flints in sand and loam.

The raised beach at Portland, which fringes the south-eastern margin of the island from 20 to 50 ft above O.D., is of especial interest because it contains marine shells as well as shingle, and is overlain by loam with non-marine shells, which in its turn is covered by ' head.' Among the shells of the raised beaches are those of periwinkles, dog-whelks, oysters and mussels, but a few species show that the climate of the time was slightly colder than that of the locality at the present time. The shingle here is composed mostly of rounded and bleached pebbles of flint and chert, but there are a few lumps of Portland Stone, rolled quartzites, and occasional boulders foreign to the district.

At the Foreland, near Bembridge, in the Isle of Wight (Fig. 36), a raised beach rests on a planed surface of the Bembridge Marls and consists of a coarse, shingly gravel, composed of flint and chert with a small proportion of material from Eocene and Lower Greensand beds.

A raised beach of shingle and sand also overlies the gravel with erratics, the mud deposits and the estuarine beds in the Selsey peninsula. Here the shingle is covered by Coombe Deposit.

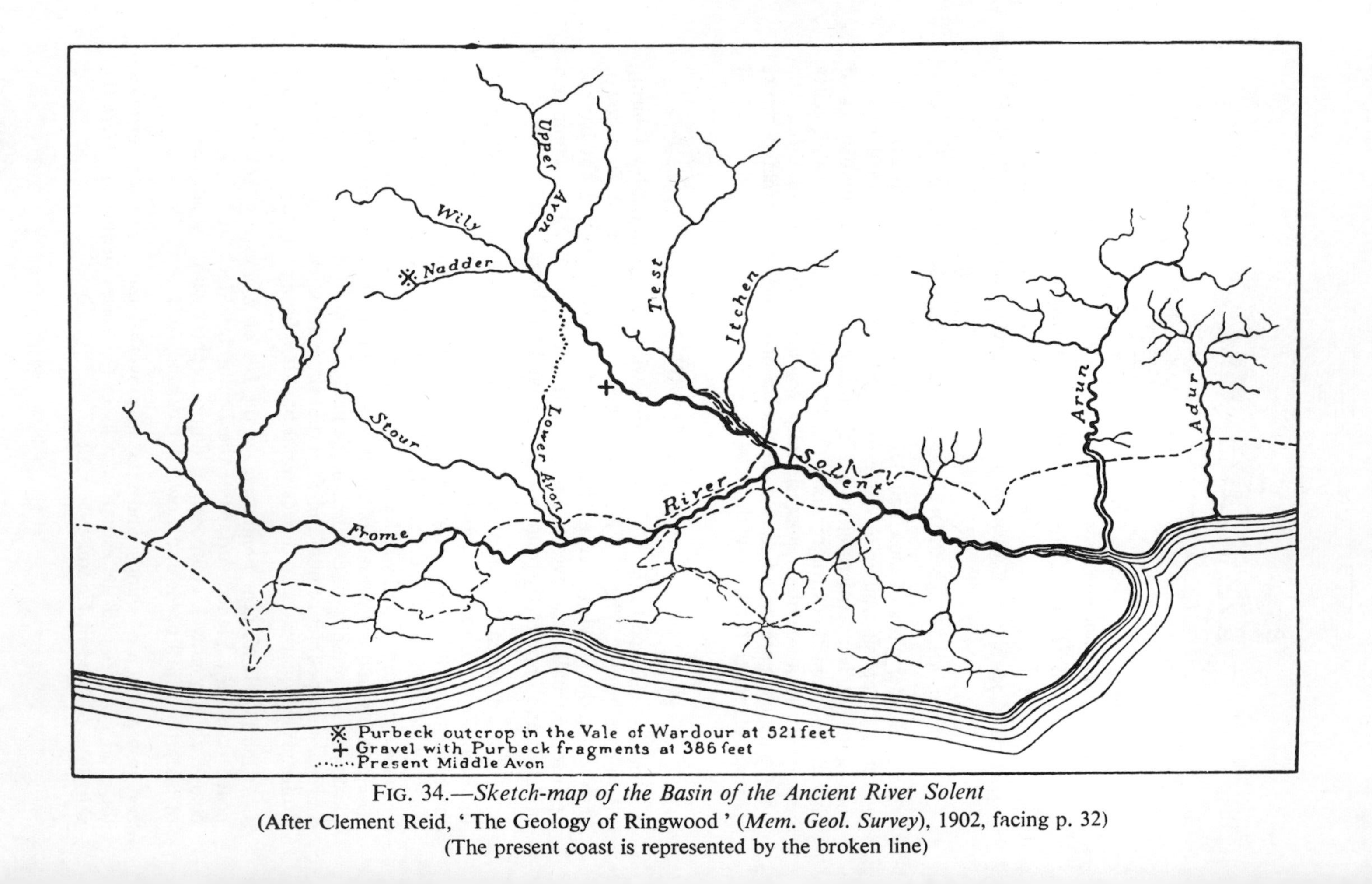

FIG. 34.—*Sketch-map of the Basin of the Ancient River Solent*
(After Clement Reid, 'The Geology of Ringwood' (*Mem. Geol. Survey*), 1902, facing p. 32)
(The present coast is represented by the broken line)

PLATEAU GRAVEL

The term 'Plateau Gravel' is used to indicate a wide range of gravel-spreads which occupy areas between valleys. These gravels stand at heights varying from above 400 ft O.D. down to 100 ft O.D. or less, and are of more than one age. The highest gravels, as already mentioned, are of considerable age, but those occupying lower plateaux or terraces are much later in date and their material has been derived from the destruction of higher series. Plateau Gravels are in part of fluviatile origin, but the streams that produced them were obviously of much greater volume than the streams of to-day. The constituents of the gravels consist of subangular flints mixed with flint pebbles and other materials derived from Eocene deposits; occasionally Palaeolithic flint implements are found. In Hampshire there are three chief areas of Plateau Gravel: those of the Bournemouth, the New Forest and the Southampton Plateaux. Isolated patches occur in Dorset, Wiltshire and the Isle of Wight, and are obviously relics of extensive sheets.

VALLEY GRAVEL; BRICKEARTH; COOMBE DEPOSIT; HEAD

Valley Gravels differ from the Plateau deposits chiefly in their distribution, being disposed along parts of existing valleys. They occur as gently inclined sheets or terraces bordering the modern alluvium but well above it (up to 50 ft), so that they cannot have been laid down by the rivers under existing conditions. In structure they are similar to Plateau Gravels, and their constituents are the materials of the latter, redistributed after considerable deepening of the valleys.

Coombe Deposit is mostly a structureless accumulation of chalk and flints in a chalky or clayey ground-mass; some of it is cemented by calcareous material and weathers into a stony loam. It appears in some cases to be the product of heavy rains acting on a frozen surface of Chalk or other deposit; in others to have originated by slumping. Thus, it varies from place to place and the name is therefore indicative of the mode of origin rather than the constituent materials. Often Coombe Deposit passes into Brickearth.

Brickearth is a brown loam, consisting of a mixture of quartz and flint-sand and ferruginous clay. Sometimes finely-divided chalk is present, as also scattered flints and gravelly seams. It is evidently a flood deposit, but there are often no signs of bedding. It occurs on the coastal plain below Fareham and Portsdown and also on Portsea Island. Evidence of an interesting assemblage of Pleistocene animals, whose remains were associated with a Palaeolithic implement, has been found in a brickearth at Fisherton, near Salisbury. Among the animals were the mammoth, woolly rhinoceros, cave lion, bison, hyaena and arctic species such as the musk-ox, reindeer and lemming. The brickearth occurs at a lower level than the Palaeolithic gravels and was probably formed after them.

Head is broken-up material (angular debris) that has travelled down sloping ground. It was probably formed under very cold conditions during a low sea-level. Vertebrate remains, including the mammoth, horse and woolly rhinoceros, have been found in the Head at Encombe in the Isle of Purbeck. Some temperate shells have been found in this deposit at Portland, but have

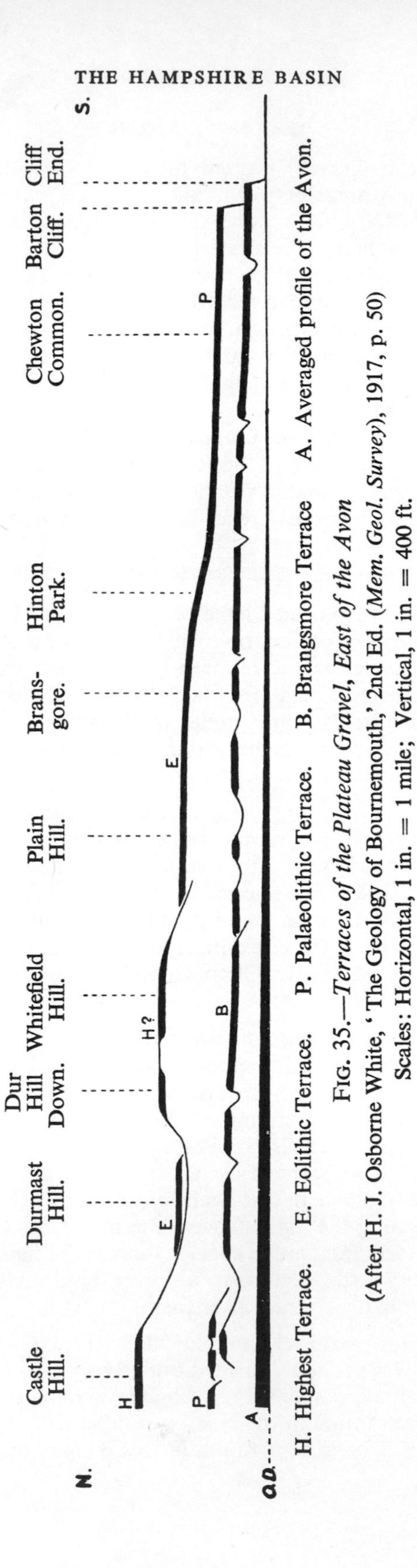

H. Highest Terrace. E. Eolithic Terrace. P. Palaeolithic Terrace. B. Brangsmore Terrace A. Averaged profile of the Avon.

FIG. 35.—*Terraces of the Plateau Gravel, East of the Avon*

(After H. J. Osborne White, 'The Geology of Bournemouth,' 2nd Ed. (*Mem. Geol. Survey*), 1917, p. 50)

Scales: Horizontal, 1 in. = 1 mile; Vertical, 1 in. = 400 ft.

been introduced into it in course of its formation. An interesting example in the Isle of Wight, at Freshwater Bay, consists of chalky gravel and loam, and contains freshwater shells and remains of the mammoth.

THE CHESIL BANK

One of the most striking features of the south coast is the great shingle ridge known as the Chesil Beach or Bank (Pl. VIII A). The pebbles of this huge storm-beach are mostly of flint and chert, with some quartzites and a very small admixture of fragments of local Jurassic limestone; pieces of rocks that can be matched in areas to the west as far as Cornwall are also included. The various constituents arrived in the area at different periods, some by way of the Tertiary deposits; but their mixing in the Bank took place in geologically recent times. From a study of these pebbles it has been concluded that the deposit is a result of the blending of material from the Portland raised beach with pebbles from terrace-gravels of an extinct river that ran along the Fleet valley; and that this took place when the valley was captured by marine erosion. Subsequently the pebbles were sorted by the action of sea-waves, so that now they increase in size eastwards, the difference between the size of those near Abbotsbury and those near Portland being considerable. At the Abbotsbury end the Bank is 170 yd wide and increases in width to 200 yd at the Portland end; while its height increases from nearly 23 ft above High Water Mark at Abbotsbury to 42 ft at the Portland end. The extent of the Beach is noted elsewhere (p. 95).

ALLUVIUM AND PEAT

The most modern deposit of rivers, or of the sea near estuaries, is called alluvium. Alluvium spread by rivers in flood-time is mostly greyish loam and consists of the fine washings of the strata and the superficial deposits in the basins of the streams; sometimes it includes bands of gravel or seams of shells. It occupies areas of varying width along the borders of streams.

In places near the coast the alluvium consists of bluish silty mud, often crowded with shells, such as *Scrobicularia plana* and *Cardium edule* (the common cockle).

Peat is closely associated with inland alluvium and in places a lateral passage can be traced. It occurs on wide tracts on low-lying marshy ground, and sometimes includes trunks of trees.

BLOWN SAND

This material is found in large quantities on the coast. It accumulates on the spits near Poole Harbour and on the low ground of the Western and Eastern Yar. It is found also on the top of cliffs in the south of the Isle of Wight between Atherfield and Blackgang. Here it consists of material from the Lower Greensand that has been blown from the cliff-face, the surface of which, as in Ladder Chine, has been sculptured by its scouring action.

THE HISTORY OF THE SUPERFICIAL DEPOSITS

We have seen that during Eocene and Oligocene times the area was gradually and intermittently subsiding. In the succeeding Period—the Miocene—the downward movement was checked, and one of upward movement ensued. The uplift was accompanied by localized folding of the strata, which produced a series of great ridges and furrows with a general trend from west to east. This process, which began after the accumulation of the Chalk and before Eocene times, was so slow that it is most unlikely that the full thickness of the uplifted strata ever stood high above the general level, for denudation was then in active progress. The structures produced by the folding (described on p. 86) formed the basis of the present land-features, but subsequent modelling has been so extensive as almost to obscure it. Apart from the fact that earth-movements were in active progress in our country during Miocene times, we know little except that it was then a land-surface, for we have no deposits to tell their story.

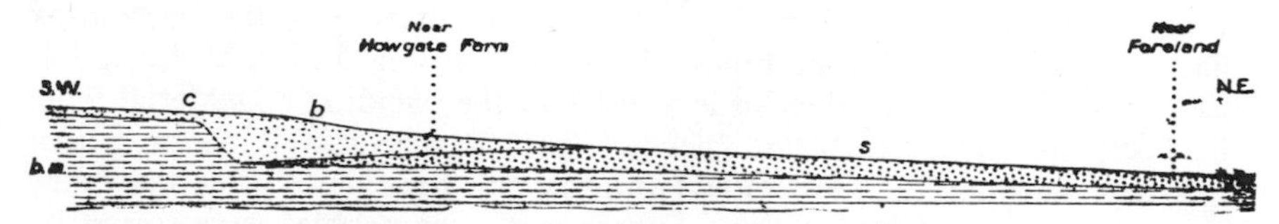

c. Buried cliff. *b*. Brickearth. *s*. Shingle of Raised Beach. *b.m.* Bembridge Marls, in which the raised-beach platform is cut.

FIG. 36.—*Section of the Raised Beach at the Foreland near Bembridge*

(After H. J. Osborne White, ' A Short Account of the Geology of the Isle of Wight ' (*Mem. Geol. Survey*), 1921, p. 177). Distance about ⅓ mile. Vertical scale, 1 in. = 210 ft.

After Miocene times two major geological periods intervened before the Recent epoch began. These were the Pliocene (Greek, *pleion*, more; *kainos*, recent) and the Pleistocene (*pleistos*, most; *kainos*, recent) periods. In the absence of fossiliferous Pliocene deposits in the area, the history of this part of the country during the period must be largely a matter of conjecture. Probably all, except the Recent, superficial deposits are of Pleistocene age, according to the new classification. Among the earliest are the spreads of high-lying gravels (Plateau Gravels), which are the relics of a drainage system that was the forerunner of that now in existence, were obviously laid down before the gravels of lower terraces, which can be dated by means of the flint implements of Early Man that are found in them. The flint implements are called Palaeoliths, and the term Palaeolithic is applied to the gravels that contain them and the terraces on which they stand. Interesting changes, however, have taken place during and after Pliocene times. Mr. W. D. Varney, in an interesting discussion of the geological history of the Vale of Pewsey, draws attention to high-lying gravel-patches near the Bradford Gorge, and in discussing the provenance of some of the constituent pebbles is led to postulate the former existence of a river that flowed eastwards from the Welsh uplands. It seems likely that this old river was a tributary or the main stream of what Clement Reid called the ' Southampton River,' part of the course of which is marked by the present Southampton Water. Reid thought that the Southampton River was joined by the head waters of the Avon, and visualized an ancient river system as set out in Fig. 34 (p. 78). Henry Bury, however, disagreed with this view and maintained that the hypothesis that the present Avon had a double origin has no evidence whatever to support it.

Meanwhile the general configuration of the country was approaching that of the present day. The larger rivers occupied their present valleys but the Isle of Wight was still part of the mainland, its separation taking place at a later date (in comparatively recent times), after the Chalk ridge between Studland and the Needles was breached. The land extended much farther to the south than at present, for the rivers of the Isle of Wight originated when the strata there were in the form of an arch much higher than the present hills. The two rivers Yar are obviously truncated, and the Western Yar shows clearly by the size of its valley and the height of the hills through which it has cut its way, that it must have drained a large area to the south.

Remains of Pleistocene vertebrates have been found from time to time in the area, and one interesting record is that of bones and teeth found in water-borne gravel near the top of an escarpment in a plateau of Chalk at Dewlish, 6 miles north-east of Dorchester. Mr. J. N. Carreck considers that most of these are referable to the Southern Elephant, *Mammuthus* (*Archidiskodon*) *meridionalis*, and are therefore of Lower Pleistocene age. A few teeth are either of '*Elephas*' cf. *antiquus* (the broad-plated form) or an *antiquus* — like variant of *M. meridionalis*. The occurrence of the latter species at Dewlish is unique in the South of England.

During the Pleistocene epoch great changes in climate and sea-level took place over the area. Changes of sea-level are proved by the presence of 'raised beaches' or ancient shore-lines preserved at different levels. Such raised beaches have long been known at Portsdown, Portland and near Bembridge, in the Isle of Wight. Recently Professor L. S. Palmer and Lt.-Col. J. H. Cooke have discussed raised beaches at levels of 100 ft, 50 ft and 15 ft, respectively, above O.D. in the Portsmouth area. Here each is marked by a bluff or degraded platform, the first platform extending from the coast to the base of the 50-ft bluff seen on the southern slopes of Portsdown Hill, and the second extending from about the 50-ft to the 100-ft contour, being then bounded by a bluff that comes into our area from the South Downs and is represented by similar features in the valleys of the Itchen, Test, Avon, Stour and Frome. The deposits associated with these terraces have been studied in detail by these investigators, with results that throw light on the climatic conditions of the time and on the occupation of the area by Early Man.

One early Pleistocene deposit in the area lies near the shore in the Selsey peninsula. This is of special significance because it gives some indication of conditions in the area when the rest of the country was undergoing the rigours of the Glacial period. No ice-sheet covered our area, although some high-lying gravels show contortions usually associated with the movement of frozen soil. But drift-ice off the coast was stranded on the low-lying shores near Selsey, where it dropped its load of erratics. These erratics, which originally became incorporated with the ice when it was forming on the shores, include boulders of rocks foreign to the district, and many of them several tons in weight. They were undoubtedly brought from distant parts, because among them are masses of Bembridge Limestone and Upper Greensand chert from the Isle of Wight, and igneous rocks probably from the Channel Islands and the coast of Brittany. One of the blocks of Eocene sandstone from Bognor Ledge bears marks of scratching by ice. This bed with erratics extends along the foreshore from Selsey to Lee-on-Solent, but has been eroded in places.

Above the erratic-bed at Selsey is a marine mud with many fossils, mostly shells, which indicate a change to a warm climate. Remains of the straight-tusked elephant (*Palaeoloxodon* [*Elephas*] *antiquus*) have also been found in this mud. The marine mud is succeeded by estuarine and *Scrobicularia* beds, which are found also at West Wittering and Stone, and have yielded remains of *Palaeoloxodon* [*Elephas*] *antiquus*, *Coelodonta* [*Rhinoceros*], many shells and plants.

It has been considered likely that the marine mud with fossils indicating a warm climate was laid down at the same time as the 100-ft beach was formed. Evidence of warm climate is found in both, and early Palaeolithic implements (Acheulian) have been found in deposits associated with both. The next stage in beach formation was that of the 50-ft terrace. The higher beach would then be dry land and, the climate being very cold, Coombe Deposit would be formed; this deposit, in fact, overlies the 100-ft beach. At the same time littoral sands were being laid down on the 15-ft level. Brickearth then spread over both the 100-ft and the 50-ft deposits. Continued sinking of the sea accompanied by cold conditions caused the formation of a second Coombe Deposit at both levels, while a deposit which is now a raised beach was being accumulated at 15 feet. The sinking of the sea still continuing, a brickearth and then Coombe Deposit formed over the lowest and newest beach, as well as over the land at higher levels. Thus Coombe Deposit accumulated once at the lowest level and twice at the intermediate level, while on the 100-ft level the land, having been above sea the longest, has three layers of Coombe Deposit. A brickearth succeeds the last Coombe Deposit on all these levels and is overlain by a modern accumulation.

Meanwhile these changes in climate and sea-level were reflected inland by the deepening and widening of the river-valleys; lower terraces were formed and were overspread with gravel and brickearth, often containing remains of the mammoth. Early Man was now well established in the area, and the tools and weapons that he fashioned out of flint or chert got washed into the gravels. To a certain extent these flint implements, especially when unworn, give some clue to the age of the gravel that contains them. Implements of early Palaeolithic types have been found in abundance along the course of the Avon, near Salisbury; while the Stour Valley gravels around Bournemouth have yielded numerous hand-axes. The gravels of the Test and Itchen are also well known for their implements. At the end of the Palaeolithic period the land probably stood only a few feet above its present level; and the development of the river valleys was such that the configuration of the country was much as it is at present. The coast extended farther southwards, however, and the Solent and the Southampton Water were less wide. During the succeeding period oncoming cold conditions were accompanied by lowering of sea-level. With the retreat of the sea the estuaries became freshwater channels and the lower valleys were excavated to a corresponding depth below their present bottom-level. Forests then spread over the exposed land, and as the sea rose again the valleys were filled with layers of gravel, silt, peat and mud, while periods of rest were marked by the formation of

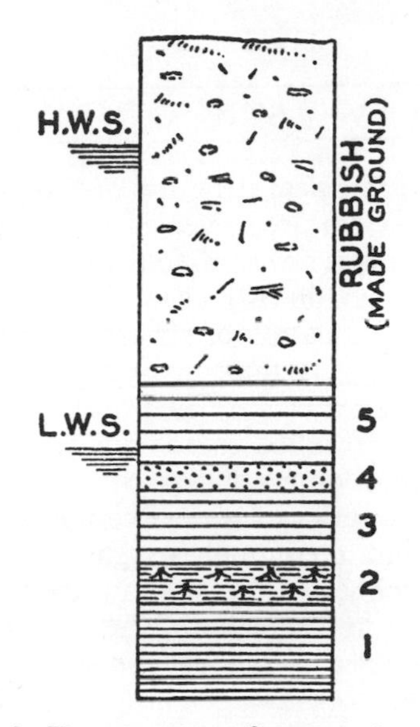

1. London Clay. 2. Forest: roots of trees and peat. 3. Blue Clay, estuarine. 4. Shingle, marine. 5. Clay, estuarine.
H. and L.W.S. High and low water, spring tides.

FIG. 37.—*Vertical section of Recent deposits, Portsmouth* (H. James)
(From *Quart. Journ. Geol. Soc.*, vol. iii, 1847, p. 250)

soils with tree trunks (Fig. 37). The final separation of the Isle of Wight from the mainland was evidently brought about by this rise in sea-level.

From time to time the now-submerged soils that were formed on the dry land have been exposed by the eroding action of rivers or the sea; they are the well-known ' submerged forests,' of which examples are found at Bournemouth, Southampton and Charmouth. One effect of the sinking of the sea and the deeper erosion and subsequent infilling of the valleys is that the rivers of Hampshire now flow through wide alluvial plains in their lower courses. Since the rise in sea-level during and after Neolithic times there have been only minor changes in the relative levels of land and sea, but erosion of the coast and the action of the waves on material worn away has produced long shingle-spits which threaten to block the outlets of harbours, and are driving the mouths of rivers eastwards. Such shingle-spits lie near the harbours of Poole and Christchurch, near Hurst Castle in the Solent, at the outlet of the Beaulieu River and at the mouth of Southampton Water.

VI. STRUCTURE

IN ITS MAIN outlines the geological structure of this part of England is simple (Pl. I). The most notable feature, revealed by mapping and seen here and there in natural sections, is a series of folds, the result of earth-movements which reached their climax in Miocene times. These movements were brought about by the accumulation of stresses in the earth's crust, and their lines mark the directions where these stresses found relief. It is interesting to note that crustal movements were in progress at the same time on the continent of Europe and resulted in the uplift of the Alps. In southern England we see only the ' outer ripples of the Alpine Storm.' Here the ripples are the result of a series of wave-like movements which gave rise to structures comparable with crests and troughs. The crests are now seen as arches (or anticlines) connected by shallow troughs; but the arches are characterized by a steep northern limb, the southern limb having only a gentle inclination. Examples of this can be seen in the Vale of Wardour, the Vale of Pewsey (Fig. 39A), Dean Hill (East of Salisbury) (Fig. 38) and in the Isle of Wight, where the Chalk of the central ridge has a steep northerly dip while in the Southern Downs it dips gently to the south. The greatest intensity of movement is observable on the Dorset Coast, where the northern limb of an important fold is overturned or broken by a fault, as along the

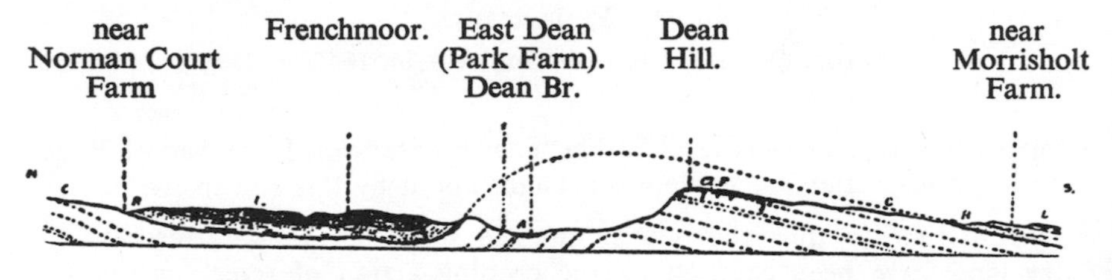

C. Chalk. *R.* Reading Beds. *L.* London Clay. *Cl.F.* Clay-with-flints. *A.* Alluvium.

FIG. 38.—*Section through Frenchmoor and Dean Hill*

(After H. J. Osborne White, ' The Geology of Winchester and Stockbridge ' (*Mem. Geol. Survey*), 1912, p. 38)

Distance, 4½ miles. Vertical scale (about 1 in. = 1,800 ft) exaggerated.

Chalk ridge in the Isle of Purbeck. An inspection of the outcrop of the Chalk on the geological map of our area (Pl. I) shows that there are three principal lines of disturbance, trending in a general way from west to east, with a slight irregular convexity northwards. On the western boundary of the Chalk are two prominent notches which correspond with the position of the Vale of Pewsey and the Vale of Wardour. A less conspicuous indentation marks the Vale of Warminster. In the south-western part of our area the regular extension of the Chalk is again interrupted where an anticline and fault bring Jurassic strata against the Chalk in the area between Abbotsbury and Weymouth Bay. Another line of disturbance can be traced eastwards along the Dorset coast and through the Isle of Purbeck; it affects also the disposition of certain strata in the Isle of Wight. The Isle of Portland is a remnant of the gently-sloping southern limb.

The Vale of Pewsey is a wedge-shaped area where the Pewsey anticline brings Upper Greensand, Gault, Lower Greensand and Kimmeridge Clay into the area of the Vale. Denudation has removed the crest of the uplifted strata (which were stretched and loosened during the process), and exposed the lower members. In this way, what was originally a geological arch is now a geographical vale, although it presents this appearance only when viewed from the high ground of the resistant Chalk on the north and south. The line of folding upon which the Pewsey anticline is situated can be traced from the Mendip Hills through the Vale of Pewsey, along the Chalk-Eocene border by Kingsclere to the Hog's Back, in Surrey. Another line of movement is marked by the Vale of Wardour, which had a similar origin to the Vale of Pewsey. This line can be traced farther west into North Devon.

Between the anticlines of the Vales of Pewsey and Wardour is the anticline of the Vale of Warminster. This anticline has a much lower structural elevation than the anticlines of Pewsey and Wardour, and does not form a long valley between the Chalk ridges as they do.

The effects of the most southerly disturbance are more plainly marked, for they are shown by the tilted and inverted beds that form such striking features on the Dorset coast near Lulworth. In the Lulworth area the Purbeck Fold gave rise to secondary structures well seen on the coast. These structures were produced because rock-beds act differentially to pressure, strong and resistant beds remaining unbroken, while weaker beds have had to accommodate themselves to movement, becoming rearranged or broken in the process. The Lulworth crumple (Pl. VI A) is a striking example of an adjustment fold, where Middle and Upper Purbeck beds have been rucked up in the process of accommodating themselves to the movement of the more resistant Portland Stone. The accommodation effects shown by the Chalk are slickensiding (fine grooving), shearing and closely-set jointing well seen west of Lulworth. A most remarkable structure, revealed in the cliff-section at Ballard Head is the unique Ballard Down Fault. This was called the Purbeck Fault by Strahan, but was afterwards for good reasons re-named by Arkell. Strahan regarded it as a southward overthrust, but Arkell thought it an attractive possibility that the curved fault-plane and the curving of the Chalk above it were produced as a form of adjustment during the folding (Fig. 39 C). In the same line as the Purbeck Fold are the vertical strata seen in Alum Bay, on the west, and in Whitecliff Bay, on the east of the Isle of Wight.

The axis of this movement, to start in the west, can be traced in an approximate W.-E. line running through Weymouth (the Weymouth anticline); eastwards is the Purbeck anticline running along the coast with its axis extending from Hobarrow Bay to Durlston Head. The Purbeck anticline runs out to sea and is evidently connected with the Brixton anticline, on the western side of the Isle of Wight. On the eastern side of the island is the Sandown anticline, separate from the Brixton anticline although due to the same movement. In South Dorset subsidiary axes are seen to the north of the main axis in the structures called the Poxwell, Sutton Poyntz and Chaldon periclines (Fig. 39 B). These structures form a series of elongated

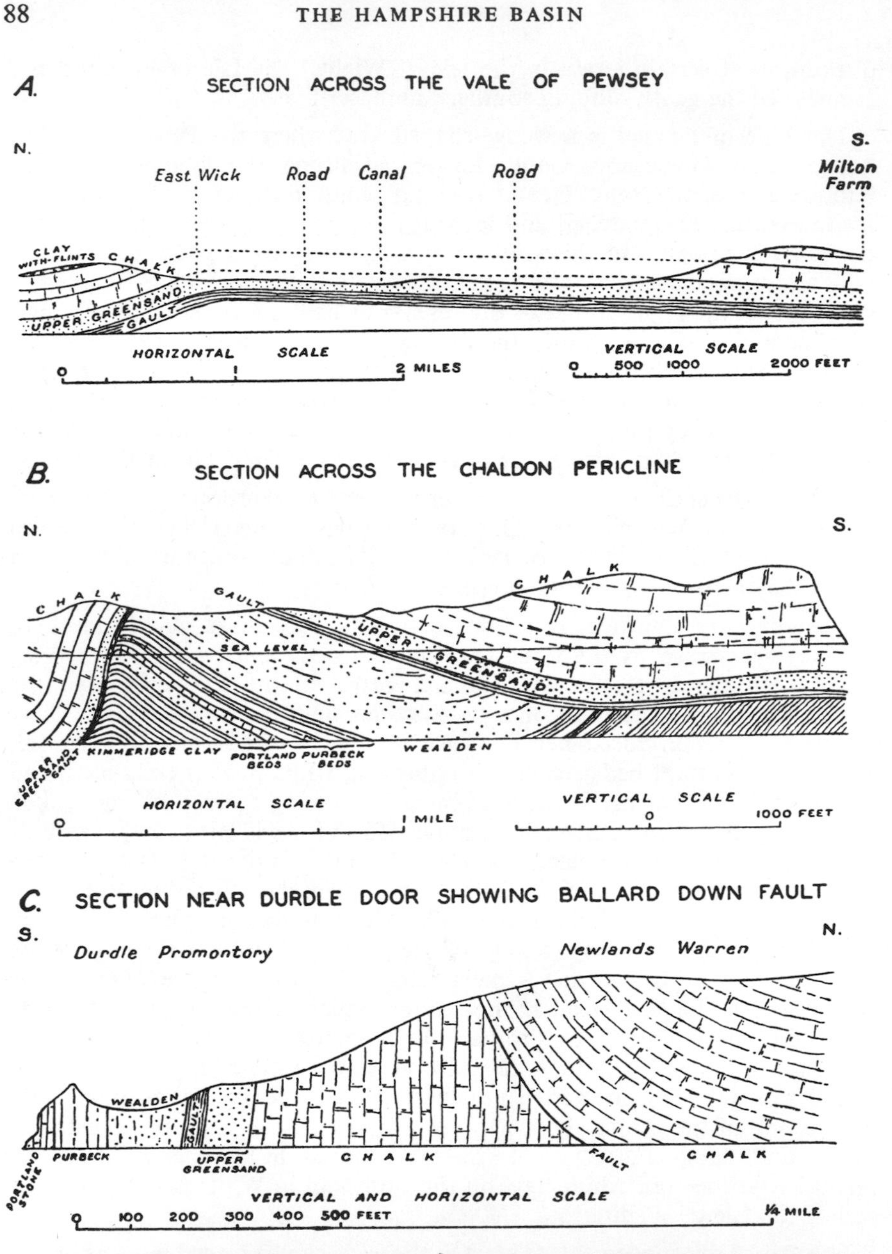

FIG. 39.—*Sections across (A) the Vale of Pewsey, (B) the Chaldon Pericline (C) the Durdle Promontory and the Ballard Down Fault*

(*A.* After W. Whitaker and F. H. Edmunds, ' The Water Supply of Wiltshire ' (*Mem. Geol. Survey*), 1925, p. 10. *B.* After A. Strahan, ' Guide to the Geological Model of the Isle of Purbeck,' 2nd Ed. (*Mem. Geol. Survey*), 1932, pl. i. *C.* After A. Strahan, ' The Geology of the Isle of Purbeck and Weymouth ' (*Mem. Geol. Survey*), 1898, pl. ix) domes with steep northern and southern slopes, like an inverted boat. Between the Poxwell anticline and the Weymouth-Purbeck anticlines is the Ringstead anticline.

Further lines of disturbance can be traced in the east of our area, and are mostly reflected in the folding of the Chalk. Two anticlines, concerned more pertinently in the uplift of the Weald, enter the Hampshire region—the anticlines of Peasemarsh and Stockbridge. The former is responsible for the high dip of the Chalk on the Hog's Back, but in our area it is practically a monocline, with the inclination of its northern limb much less steep than in the Weald. A second anticline is also traceable from the Weald; it ends just west of Stockbridge and its course is marked by a swell of downland. South of this is the Winchester anticline, which extends entirely in Chalk country from Winchester in an E.S.E. direction towards Petersfield. Much farther to the west, in the Vale of Wardour, begins another anticline, which runs through Bower Chalk, near Salisbury, and is evidently connected with the short anticline that swings round near Dean Hill (Fig. 38). Eastwards the Dean Hill anticline is continued as the Portsdown anticline, which extends south-eastwards and is marked by the uprising of the Chalk along Portsdown, whence it runs out to sea east of Bognor. The syncline bordering the Dean Hill anticline on the north is conspicuous on the map by reason of its preserving a narrow strip of Eocene beds almost entirely within the Chalk outcrop.

Recent studies on the structure of the western Weald have suggested certain modifications of the axial lines of the anticlines in that area. In particular the western extension of the Peasemarsh anticline would be modified. It is suggested that this extends only a short distance in the Chalk, and is replaced to the north by a separate anticline (the Farleigh Wallop anticline, trending E.N.E.). But for the purpose of illustrating the general structure of the area the lines on Plate I will suffice.

In the Isle of Wight, where the presence of two separate anticlines has been noted, the conspicuous widening of the outcrop of the Chalk (between Calbourne and Gatcombe) marks the area where one ends and the other begins. Minor complementary folds affecting the Tertiary strata on the northern half of the island are shown by the Bouldnor syncline and the Porchfield anticline (Fig. 40).

That the period of maximum intensity of earth-movement in the area was the Miocene is shown by the fact that the Oligocene strata are considerably affected by them, as seen in the coast-sections at either end of the Isle of Wight. In some parts of the area, however, uplift and the consequent denudation commenced earlier, because certain Eocene gravels in Dorset contain pebbles which show that the Chalk and older strata were undergoing erosion while Eocene deposits were being laid down.

In the western part of the area a still older series of anticlines and synclines can be detected; these were formed during the Cretaceous period, and are conspicuous in the neighbourhood of Weymouth. That the earth movements that gave rise to these structures took place before Upper Cretaceous times is proved by the fact that in places Jurassic and Wealden strata were tilted and eroded before the Upper Greensand and Chalk were laid down. Thus near White Nothe, on the Dorset coast at Ringstead Bay, highly

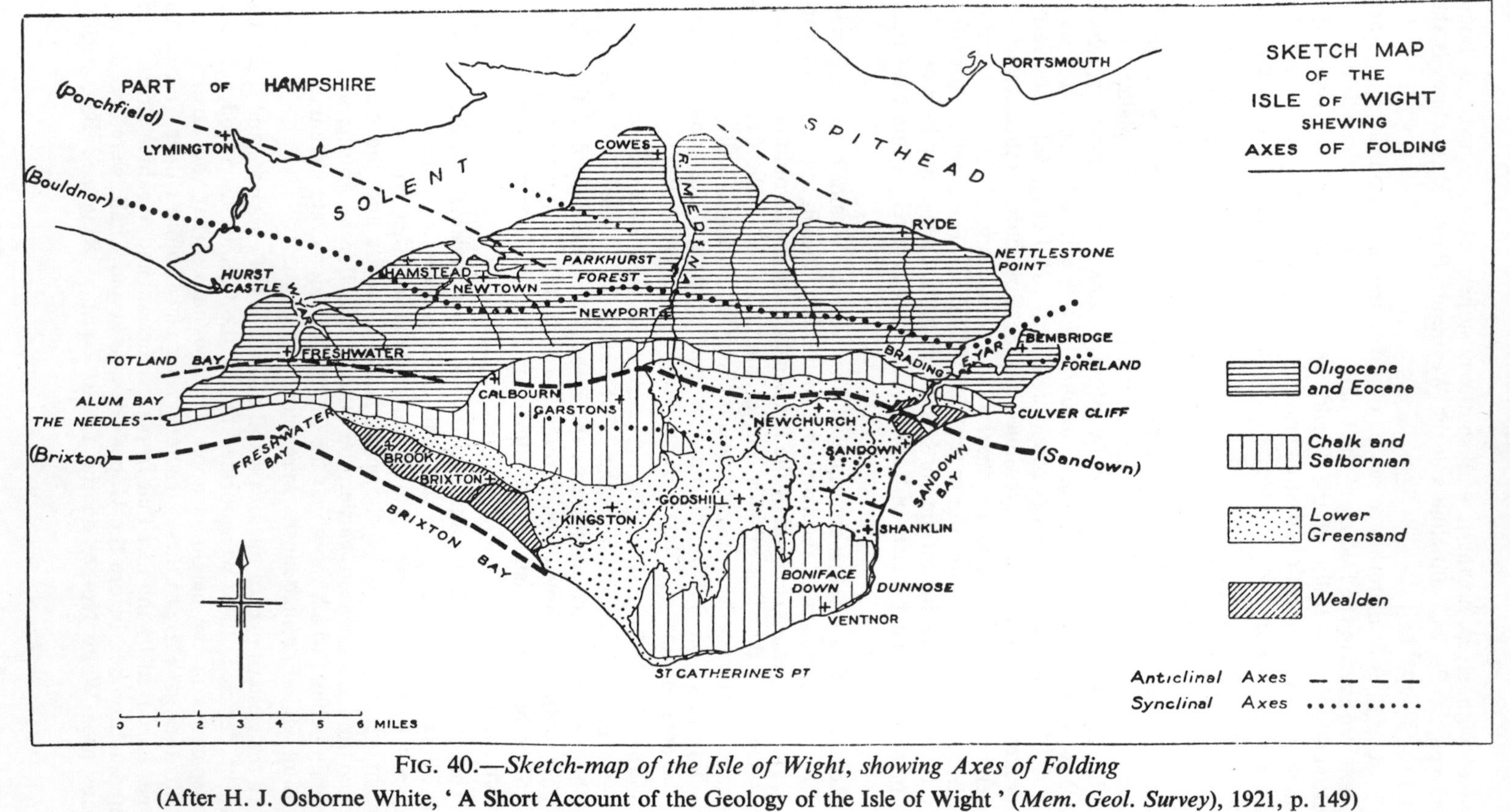

FIG. 40.—*Sketch-map of the Isle of Wight, showing Axes of Folding*
(After H. J. Osborne White, ' A Short Account of the Geology of the Isle of Wight ' (*Mem. Geol. Survey*), 1921, p. 149)

inclined Kimmeridge, Portland and Purbeck beds are overlain by Upper Greensand with a very slight dip (Pl. VII, B, and Fig. 20). Farther west also, near Abbotsbury, Forest Marble, Corallian and Kimmeridge strata were tilted and faulted before the Upper Greensand was deposited on their upturned edges (Fig. 41). To these intra-Cretaceous movements (they are post-Wealden and pre-Gault in age) can be ascribed the Osmington and Broadway anticlines, the Upton and Upwey synclines, and the Abbotsbury fault.

The structure of the Vale of Marshwood is referred to in connexion with its scenery (p. 93). The Liassic strata by the coast near Lyme Regis are affected by gentle folding and occasional faults (Fig. 1); and a disturbance in the Char valley, marked by a fault and local contortion of beds, may be due to compensatory bulging.

VII. SCENERY

SEVERAL WELL-KNOWN geographical units and a variety of scenic types are included in the area under description. Among them are the New Forest, the Isle of Wight, the Isle of Purbeck, the Chesil Bank, the Vales of Marshwood, Wardour and Pewsey and the Chalk uplands known as the Dorset Downs, Salisbury Plain and the Hampshire Downs. Of the chief geological regions it includes part of the southern end of the great Jurassic belt that runs in a north-easterly direction through England, part of the Chalk belt and the Hampshire Basin.

A wide range of physical features is thus represented, and it will be seen that these are intimately connected with the geological structure. The larger part of the area is the upland country typical of the Chalk formation. Three of the largest tracts of chalk-lands in England are included—the Hampshire Downs, Salisbury Plain and the Dorset Downs. These chalk-lands exhibit characteristic features undulating stretches with softly-rounded outlines and steep slopes, the result of long-continued subaerial denudation of a soft permeable limestone, relatively soluble by percolating water (Pl. VIIA). On the eastern border of the Hampshire Downs are the Alton Hills, rising in places to 700 ft O.D. On the northern margin of these Downs is another range of hills which passes round the southern border of the Vale of Kingsclere, rising in two places to a height of more than 900 ft O.D. These uplands consist of a succession of broad rolling downs, intersected by a branching network of valleys. Salisbury Plain is the western continuation of the Hampshire Uplands, and is not truly a plain, as its name might imply, but a wide expanse of undulating country intersected by a system of coombes and valleys (Fig. 42). It appears level only when seen from the broad ridges of which the higher part is composed. From these ridges (the remnants of a plateau) the intervening valleys cannot be seen; hence the distant ridges have the appearance of a level plain. The Dorset Downs

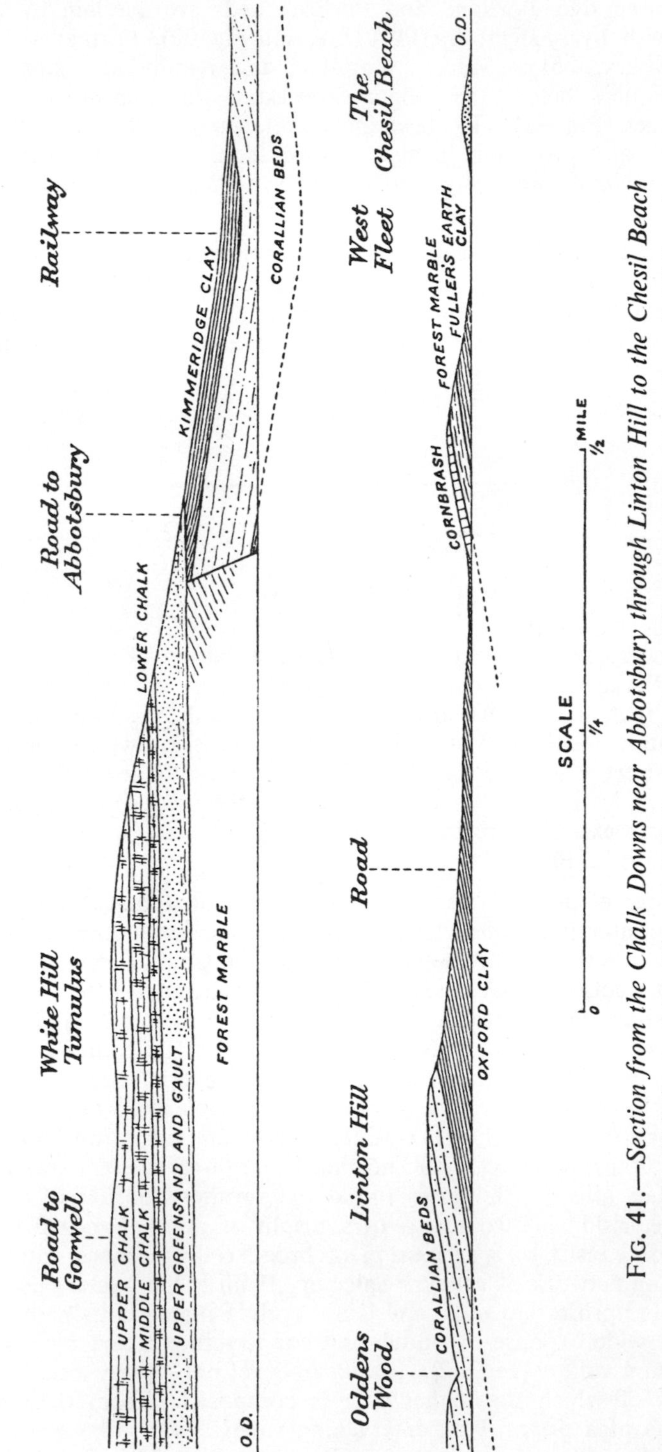

FIG. 41.—*Section from the Chalk Downs near Abbotsbury through Linton Hill to the Chesil Beach* (After W. Whitaker and W. Edwards, 'Wells and Springs of Dorset' (*Mem. Geol. Survey*), 1926, p. 4)

show the usual features of chalk uplands; they commence in the extreme south of Wiltshire, at Cranbourne Chase, an area that was originally all woodland.

Scattered over the surface of the Chalk in various parts of the area, as near the eastern borders of Hampshire, around Salisbury, and near Marlborough, are boulders of sandstone called ' Sarsens.' These Sarsens vary in size from small boulders to masses of 60-70 tons in weight, and are the remnants of deposits probably of Eocene age that have since been destroyed by denudation. They are sometimes called ' greywethers ' from their resemblance in the distance to a flock of sheep, and sometimes ' Saracens ' or ' strangers.' The name Sarsen was evidently derived from the Saxon *sar* (troublesome) and *stan* (a stone), being applied because they were a hindrance to the early clearers of the land.

In the Hampshire Basin the Chalk formation dips beneath the Tertiary strata, which are mostly soft sands and clays. Part of this basin, the New Forest, is a large area of sandy beds covered with open heath or grass land and forests of oak and pine.

In the south-western corner of our area the country west of the Chalk outcrop has been deeply excavated by stream erosion, so that the high land formed by the hard beds of chert and sandstone stands out as isolated hills, some with prominent spurs, while in the lower parts, as in the valleys near Charmouth and in the Vale of Marshwood, the land has been worn down to the level of the softer Lower Lias. In its geological structure the Vale of Marshwood is a dome, with gently sloping strata on the east and more considerable dips to the north-west, west, and south-west. Denudation has reduced it to a basin-shaped hollow, bordered by sandy beds of Middle Lias which form a low encircling ridge. Farther to the east, between Bridport and Beaminster, is the country of the Bridport Sands formation, characterized by steep-sided valleys and rounded contours. ' Sunken lanes,' due to the softness of the beds, are a typical feature of the Bridport Sands, while resistant hills and plateau-areas mark the presence of a capping of Inferior Oolite. Colmore Hill, west of Symondsbury, shows the characteristic form of the Bridport Sands when stripped of a protective covering of Inferior Oolite and trenched by river valleys. North of the Chalk Heights in Dorset, is the famous Vale of Blackmore, a well-watered area of undulating pasture land, formed largely on the Oxford Clay.

On the north-west of this the ground rises as a succession of ridges formed by the resistant strata of Cornbrash and Forest Marble, the Fuller's Earth Rock (a narrow upland) and the Inferior Oolite. Between the ridges are vales formed by the upper and lower clays of the Fuller's Earth. East of the Oxford Clay tract is the upland formed by the Corallian rocks, followed again on the east by the lower grass land of the Kimmeridge Clay, leading up to the escarpments of the Upper Greensand and Chalk. The flat land formed by the soft Kimmeridge Clay extends along the border of the Chalk and underlying beds into the Vale of Wardour, a wedge-shaped erosion-valley in the Chalk. North of this vale the Chalk rises again, extending as far as the Vale of Pewsey, which opens out into a flat plain of soft Jurassic clays through which the Avon flows. The north-eastern corner of our area is occupied by the higher ground formed by the more resistant beds of Cornbrash and Great Oolite.

The coastal parts of the area are full of interest to geologists. Except for the range of bold Chalk cliffs between White Nothe and Worbarrow Bay the coast from Lyme Regis to Swanage is bordered by Jurassic rocks. Eastwards is the less prominent coast of Hampshire.

As we look along the coast eastwards from Lyme Regis, the various beds of the Lias are seen to dip very slightly, capped by horizontal masses of resistant Upper Greensand (Pl. II A). The isolated heights of Stonebarrow

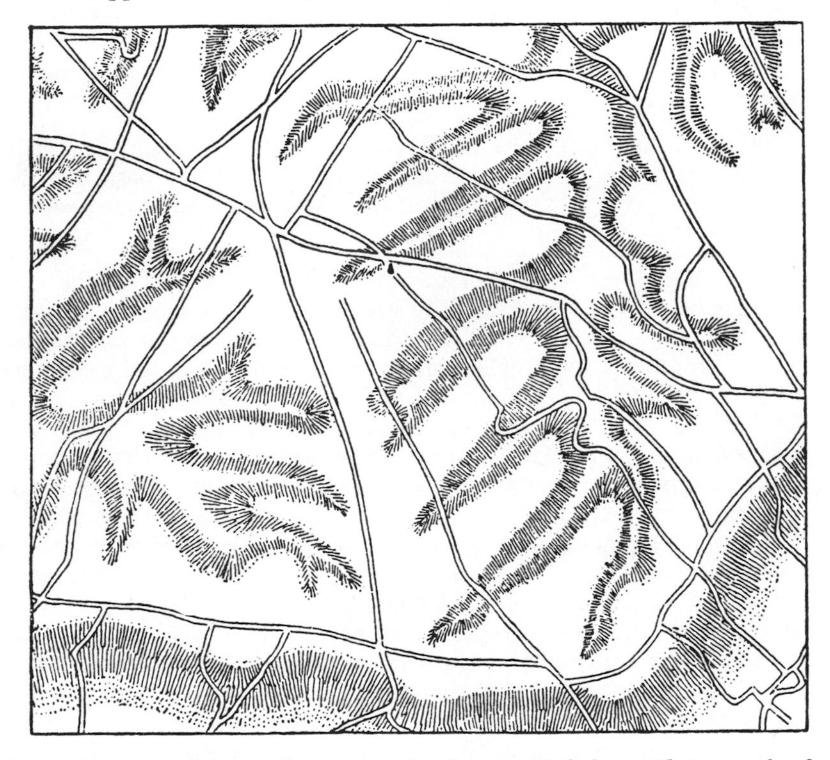

FIG. 42.—*Sketch-map of a group of valleys on Salisbury Plain, south of Urchfont and Cherrington*

(After A. J. Jukes-Browne and W. Hill, ' The Cretaceous Rocks of Britain,' vol. iii (*Mem. Geol. Survey*), 1904, p. 419)

Hill, Golden Cap and Thorncombe Beacon are due to such cappings, Golden Cap having received its name from its gilded appearance on a sunny day, the sands presenting a sharp contrast to the dark clays beneath. Between Lyme Regis and Burton Bradstock the high ground near the coast is deeply incised by streams, the most considerable being the Char, the Winniford and the Brit. Immediately west of West Bay (Bridport Harbour) the regular extension of the strata is interrupted by beds of Fuller's Earth and Forest Marble, which have been let down by dislocations of the strata (or faults). On the eastern side of the Harbour the cliffs are almost vertical or overhanging in places, being formed of the yellowish-brown Bridport Sands, wherein bands of concretionary sandstone stand out prominently among the less resistant sands (Pl. III A). East of Burton Bradstock the soft beds of the Fuller's Earth Series form a low slope running well back from the shore, and extend to near Abbotsbury, where they are terminated by a fault. Along this stretch the coast is bordered by the famous Chesil Bank. Beginning near Burton Bradstock this low ridge of pebbles extends for about 16 miles to the Isle of Portland. For six miles it is in contact with the coast; for the next eight miles eastwards it is separated from the mainland by the Fleet, a shallow salt-water lagoon.

The Fleet is connected with the sea only at its eastern end; the outline of its northern shore varies according to the nature of the strata, the soft Oxford Clay receding and the harder Cornbrash, Forest Marble and Corallian beds jutting out (Pl. VIII A). At the western end of the Fleet, in an embayment scooped out of the soft Oxford Clay and shaped by a projecting spur of hard Cornbrash, is the well-known Abbotsbury Swannery (Pl. III B). The Oxford Clay here is the commencement of a narrow tract which extends eastwards and opens out into Weymouth Bay. To the south of this, aligned in an approximate west-east direction, are ridges of the harder strata just mentioned. To the north the Corallian beds rise in prominent scarps.

The Isle of Portland (it is called an island though actually it is connected with the Chesil Bank by a ridge of blown sand and pebbles) forms a projecting bulwark, consisting of Purbeck and Portland rocks resting on Kimmeridge Clay; behind lies Portland Harbour. North of this the sea has carved Weymouth Bay out of a soft clay formation, the Oxford Clay. Corallian and Kimmeridge strata form the cliffs eastwards to Ringstead Bay, where overstepping Upper Cretaceous beds (Gault, Upper Greensand and Chalk) are brought to the shore by faulting. The Chalk forms the bold cliffs commencing near White Nothe. Eastwards tilted Chalk, forming the magnificent features of Bat's Head and Swyre Head and picturesque coves at Durdle Cove and Man o' War Cove, extends to St. Oswald's Bay, where it continues inland and reappears at Mupe Bay. At Durdle Door and along the stretch between St. Oswald's Bay and Mupe Bay the force of the waves is met by a barrier of Portland Beds. These beds are upturned, as also are the beds of Purbeck, Wealden, Gault and Upper Greensand which lie between them and the Chalk. This short stretch of coast is interrupted by the famous Lulworth Cove, which has been scooped out by the sea, for the soft Wealden beds readily gave way once the sea had entered the former seaward extension of the valley of the small stream now flowing into the Cove, through the stream-cut breach in the harder seaward rim of Portland and Purbeck rocks. The tilted and crumpled arrangement of the Purbeck and Portland beds is well seen in Stair Hole, near by to the west, where the soft strata are also being eroded (Pl. VI B).

The Chalk passes inland again in Worbarrow Bay, just past the prominent Arish Mell, and running eastwards as a narrow sinuous ridge across the Isle of Purbeck reappears north of Swanage Bay. Seaward of this ridge, folding has again brought up Upper Jurassic strata—the Kimmeridge Clay, Portland Beds and the Purbeck Beds. In the western half of this area the Kimmeridge Clay comes to the shore and forms low cliffs of blackish shaly clay with stone bands. Low-lying clay land extends inland for a variable distance until it rises to meet the steep front of the escarpment of hard Portland Stone which forms a background to this coastal tract. The high steep-walled capping of Portland Stone runs close to the shore from near Chapman's Pool to St. Alban's Head, whence with a covering of Purbeck strata it forms the cliffs eastwards to Durlston Head. To the north of this point Purbeck beds are let down by faulting and continue to Peveril Point, where the northerly dip brings the Wealden Beds to the surface. Here the less resistant character of these beds is reflected in the topography, for Swanage Bay is carved out of them. Past the narrow outcrop of Lower Greensand, Gault and Upper Greensand the ground rises again where we meet the eastern extension of the 'Hog's Back' of inclined Chalk. Just north of Ballard Point is the line of the Ballard Down fault, where steeply curved beds on the north of the fault have been brought against vertical beds. Several sea-stacks stand in the sea, detached from the parent cliff of Chalk. One is known as 'Old Harry'; 'Old Harry's Wife,' which used to stand near by, was destroyed by the sea in 1896.

The Chalk ridge is terminated on the north by the Foreland; thence for a short distance northwards the coast changes abruptly; the Chalk disappears beneath Lower Tertiary beds, and sand dunes extend to the entrance of Poole Harbour. These sand dunes commence again at the other side of the narrow entrance to the harbour and extend to the mainland, here consisting of soft Tertiary strata. From just west of Bournemouth to Milford, a stretch of coast along which erosion is particularly rapid in certain parts (being at the rate of one foot a year at Bournemouth and considerably more near Highcliff), the cliffs are cut by deep ravines called chines or 'bunneys.' While erosion is active in some parts, however, the action of the tides in other places causes the detritus to accumulate in unstable sandbanks and shingle spits.

Bournemouth Bay has been carved out of soft Eocene strata, which are capped in most places by Plateau Gravels. The cliffs are continued in the detached ridge of Hengistbury Head, and after an interval of two miles of low-lying ground near Christchurch are continued again at Highcliff, in Christchurch Bay. There the beds are inclined gently to the east and lead first to the famous section of Barton Beds and then to the section of Lower Headon Beds between Hordle and Milford. From near Milford to Southampton Water the coast is low, and bordered by level tracts of mud. East of Southampton Water the coast is almost uniformly flat and low-lying.

The Tertiary strata of the Hampshire Basin occupy an approximately triangular area, extending from near Salisbury to Dorchester on the west and to Havant on the east. Projecting in the south-eastern extremity is the long grassy Chalk ridge of Portsdown, the site of a recent boring to locate petroleum. For the most part the Tertiary strata are soft sands and clays, and being of a less resistant nature than the rest of the formations exposed in our area they present a marked scenic contrast. Over wide areas where covered with patches of Plateau Gravel they form flat-topped plateaux and terraces, intersected by valleys and much eroded.

The Tertiary strata of the mainland are continued in the northern part of the Isle of Wight, which is separated by a narrow strip of water—the Solent-Spithead strait. Within the comparatively small area of the island the Cretaceous and Tertiary formations are well represented, and give rise to a variety of scenery on a small though often relatively striking scale. The dominant topographical feature is a narrow belt of high downland which extends from east to west and is the main structural axis of the island. This axis (the ' backbone of the island,' as it has been called) is formed by highly inclined Chalk, and divides the island into two markedly-different areas. The northern area is of very slight relief, but marked here and there by tracts of woodland; patches of gravelly plateaux cap the higher ground along the northern coast; the shores on this side, especially on the east, are low and shelving. South of the central downland the relief of the country is more varied. The greater part (formed of Lower Greensand) is an undulating vale with sharp rises here and there. At the southern extremity of the island are the Southern Downs, formed of Chalk gently dipping to the south and once continuous with the central ridge. On the inland side of the Downs are scarps and deep embayments; the crests are smoothly rounded. Seawards the steep slope of the Chalk surface passes into a tract of terraced ground formed by the slipping of the strata above the unctuous Gault. The attractive scenery of the Undercliff is due to slipped masses of Upper Greensand and Chalk that have broken away and slid along the inclined surface of the Gault, rendered slippery by the outflow of springs.

The principal rivers, the Medina and the Eastern and Western Yar, commence their courses on the Southern downs and flow northwards. West of the Medina the coast rises gradually and becomes bolder; definite cliffs extend from Cliff End on the north-west of the island, past the Needles and round the south coast as far as the Foreland at the eastern end. These cliffs are cut into here and there by chines, or notches formed by rivulets (Fig. 18). On account of its superior hardness the Chalk forms bold cliffs on the coast, and its western extremity is marked by magnificent sea-stacks—the Needles.

The lozenge-shaped outline of the Isle of Wight is due to the presence of the central ridge of Chalk running from west to east, the softer strata north and south of the ends of this ridge having been worn away by marine erosion much more than the Chalk itself. On the western end of the central ridge the Needles afford clear evidence of the stout resistance of the Chalk in the unceasing battle between land and sea. Formerly, the Chalk of the central ridge was continuous with that of the Purbeck Hills, and the separation of the island from the mainland took place when an estuary on the north was invaded by the sea, while on the south a stream, probably flowing from the south (Fig. 34), cut through the Chalk. Subsequent submergence of the area would enable the sea to complete the work thus begun. The process is illustrated by the Purbeck peninsula, where there is already the tidal estuary on the northern side. If the Chalk were breached, say, near Worbarrow Bay, and a subsidence took place, the sea would soon convert the peninsula into a true island, comparable with the Isle of Wight.

An EXHIBIT illustrating the Geology and Scenery of the district described in this volume is set out on the Ground Floor of the Museum of Practical Geology, Exhibition Road, South Kensington, London, S.W.7.

VIII. GEOLOGICAL SURVEY MAPS AND MEMOIRS DEALING WITH THE HAMPSHIRE BASIN AND ADJOINING AREAS

MAPS

(*a*) On the Scale of 4 miles to 1 inch: *colour-printed.*

Sheet 19. Bath, Guildford, Abingdon, Southampton.
„ 23. Bournemouth, Isle of Wight, Selsey Bill.
Small parts of the area are on the following:—
Sheet 18. Bristol, Crewkerne, etc.
„ 22. Lyme Regis, etc.

(*b*) On the Scale of 1 mile to 1 inch:

New Series Sheets, colour-printed. Price 5*s*. 0*d*. each.

Sheets 266. Marlborough. 267. Hungerford. 282. Devizes. 283. Andover. 284. Basingstoke.
Sheets 298. Salisbury. 299. Winchester. 300. New Alresford.
Sheets 312. Yeovil. 313. Shaftesbury. 314. Ringwood. 315. Southampton. 316. Havant.
Sheets 327. Bridport. 328. Dorchester. 329. Bournemouth. 330. Lymington. 331. Portsmouth. 332. Bognor, Selsey, etc.
Sheets 341. West Fleet. 342. Weymouth. 343. Swanage.
Special Sheet. Isle of Wight and Part of Mainland. Price 7*s*. 0*d*.

(*c*) On the Scale of 6 inches to 1 mile:

The greater part of the area represented by New Series one-inch scale maps is also represented by maps on the six-inch scale. These are not published, but are in manuscript form, and may be consulted in the Geological Survey Library. Uncoloured photo-copies may be supplied on special order.

MEMOIRS

(*a*) District Memoirs:

Isle of Wight, A Short Account of the Geology of the. By H. J. Osborne White, 1921.
Purbeck, Isle of, and Weymouth. By A. Strahan. 1898.
Weymouth, Swanage, Corfe and Lulworth, The Geology of the Country around. By W. J. Arkell, with contributions by C. W. Wright and H. J. Osborne White, 1947. Price 25*s*. 0*d*.
Weymouth, Swanage, Corfe and Lulworth. Addenda and Corrigenda. 1952. Price 3*d*.

(*b*) Sheet Memoirs (*New Series*):

Memoirs in explanation of the New Series Maps have been published:—

Sheets 312 and 327. Bridport and Yeovil. Published 1959. Price 30*s*. 0*d*.
Sheets 341, 342 and 343 are covered by the Weymouth Memoir listed above.

(*c*) Water Supply Memoirs:

Hampshire. 1910. Wiltshire. 1925. Dorset. 1926.

(*d*) General Memoirs:

Cretaceous Rocks of Britain:

Vol. I.—The Gault and Upper Greensand of England. By A. J. Jukes-Browne, with contributions by W. Hill. 1900.
Vol. II.—The Lower and Middle Chalk of England. By A. J. Jukes-Browne, with contributions by W. Hill. 1903.
Vol. III.—The Upper Chalk of England. By A. J. Jukes-Browne, with contributions by W. Hill. 1904.

Jurassic Rocks of Britain:

Vol. III.—The Lias of England and Wales (Yorkshire excepted). By H. B. Woodward. 1893.

Vol. IV.—The Lower Oolitic Rocks of England (Yorkshire excepted). By H. B. Woodward. 1894.

Vol. V.—The Middle and Upper Oolitic Rocks of England (Yorkshire excepted). By H. B. Woodward. 1895.

(*e*) **Special Reports on Mineral Resources:**

The following contain reference to the Hampshire Basin area:—

Vol. VII.—Mineral Oil, Kimmeridge Oil-shale, etc. (1920, 2nd Ed.).
Vol XXXI.—Ball Clays. (1929). *5s. 0d.*

(*f*) **Guide:**

Geological Model of the Isle of Purbeck. By A. Strahan, 2nd Ed., 1932.

PHOTOGRAPHS

A large series of photographs illustrative of the geology of the area (of which Plates II—VIII are examples) are deposited for public reference in the Library of the Geological Survey. Copies of these photographs and lantern slides are supplied at standard rates.

NOTE

Stocks of Geological Survey Publications were destroyed during the late war. Reprinting is in hand, and many of the 1-inch scale maps are now on sale. Few memoirs, however, are obtainable, and the above list is included primarily for reference purposes. The price is given only of those memoirs now available for purchase.

Printed in England for Her Majesty's Stationery Office by Ebenezer Baylis and Son Ltd
Worcester, and London
Dd 289687 K60

LIST OF HANDBOOKS ON THE REGIONAL GEOLOGY OF GREAT BRITAIN

ENGLAND AND WALES:

Northern England (*4th Edition*, 1971) . . .	40p
London and Thames Valley (*3rd Edition*, 1960) .	30p
Central England (*3rd Edition*, 1969) . . .	40p
East Yorkshire and Lincolnshire (1948) . .	45p
The Wealden District (*4th Edition*, 1965) . .	30p
The Welsh Borderland (*3rd Edition*, 1971) . .	40p
South-West England (*4th Edition*, 1975) . .	70p
Hampshire Basin and Adjoining Areas (*3rd Edition*, 1960)	95p
East Anglia and Adjoining Areas (*4th Edition*, 1961)	35p
South Wales (*3rd Edition*, 1970)	50p
North Wales (*3rd Edition*, 1961)	30p
The Pennines and Adjoining Areas (*3rd Edition*, 1954)	45p
Bristol and Gloucester District (*2nd Edition*, 1948) .	45p

SCOTLAND:

Grampian Highlands (*3rd Edition*, 1966) . .	50p
Northern Highlands (*3rd Edition*, 1960) . .	35p
South of Scotland (*3rd Edition*, 1971) . . .	50p
Midland Valley of Scotland (*2nd Edition*, 1948) .	32½p
Tertiary Volcanic Districts (*3rd Edition*, 1961) .	35p
Orkney and Shetlands	in press

The above prices do not include postage

The handbooks are obtainable from the Geological Museum, Institute of Geological Sciences, Exhibition Road, South Kensington, SW7 2DE, and from

HER MAJESTY'S STATIONERY OFFICE

AT THE ADDRESSES ON COVER PAGE IV OR THROUGH BOOKSELLERS